MEI STRUCTURED MATHEMATICS

THIRD EDITION

Differential Equations

John Berry
Ted Graham
Peter Mitchell
Roger Porkess

Series Editor: Roger Porkess

Hodder Murray

A MEMBER OF THE HODDER H

Acknowledgements

The publishers would like to thank the following for permission to reproduce copyright material:

Michael Donne/Science Photo Library (page 1, top); Emma Lee, Life File Photographic Library Ltd (page 1, middle); Frank Lukasseck/Zeta/Corbis (page 1, bottom); Robert Harding Picture Library Ltd/Alamy (left page 19); Alfred Pasieka/Science Photo Library (page 19, right); Mary Evans Picture Library (both page 33, page 63); Gunter Marx Photography/CORBIS (page 70); Jim Richardson/Corbis (page 103, left); Associated Press (page 103, right); Michael Prince/Corbis (page 103, middle); Alfa Romeo (page 115); Topham/PA (page 124, left); A Lambert Photography (page 124, right); Associated Press/EMPICS (page 125); Kit Kittle/Corbis (page 142); Mehau Kulyk/Science Photo Library (page 158).

OCR accept no responsibility whatsoever for the accuracy or method of working in the answers given.

Every effort has been made to trace all copyright holders, but if any have been inadvertently overlooked the publishers will be pleased to make the necessary arrangements at the first opportunity.

Although every effort has been made to ensure that website addresses are correct at time of going to press, Hodder Murray cannot be held responsible for the content of any website mentioned in this book. It is sometimes possible to find a relocated web page by typing in the address of the home page for a website in the URL window of your browser.

Hodder Headline's policy is to use papers that are natural, renewable and recyclable and made from wood grown in sustainable forests. The logging and manufacturing processes are expected to conform to the environmental regulations of the country of origin.

Orders: please contact Bookpoint Ltd, 130 Milton Park, Abingdon, Oxon OX14 4SB.
Telephone: (44) 01235 827720. Fax: (44) 01235 400454. Lines are open 9am to 5pm, Monday to Saturday, with a 24-hour message-answering service. Visit our website at www.hoddereducation.co.uk.

Impression number	10	9	8	7	6	5	4	3	2	
Year		2011	2010	2009	2008	2007	2006			

Typeset in 10.5pt Minion by Pantek Arts Ltd., Maidstone, Kent
Printed in Malta

A catalogue record for this title is available from the British Library

ISBN-10: 0340 905 271
ISBN-13: 978 0340 905 272

Printed in Malta for Hodder Education, a division of
Hodder Headline, 338 Euston Road, London NW1 3BH

MEI Structured Mathematics

Mathematics is not only a beautiful and exciting subject in its own right but also one that underpins many other branches of learning. It is consequently fundamental to the success of a modern economy.

MEI Structured Mathematics is designed to increase substantially the number of people taking the subject post-GCSE, by making it accessible, interesting and relevant to a wide range of students.

It is a credit accumulation scheme based on 45 hour units which may be taken individually or aggregated to give Advanced Subsidiary (AS) and Advanced GCE (A Level) qualifications in Mathematics and Further Mathematics. The units may also be used to obtain credit towards other types of qualification.

The course is examined by OCR (previously the Oxford and Cambridge Schools Examination Board) with examinations held in January and June each year.

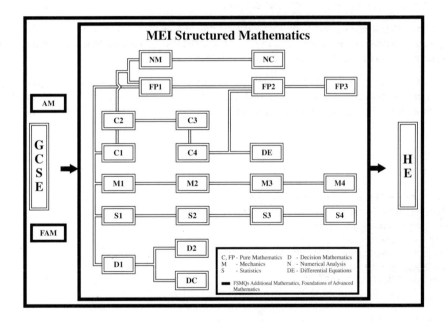

This is one of the series of books written to support the course. Its position within the whole scheme can be seen in the diagram above.

Mathematics in Education and Industry (MEI) is an independent curriculum development body which aims to promote links between education and industry in mathematics. MEI produce relevant examination specifications at GCSE, AS and A Level (including Further Mathematics) and for Free Standing Mathematics Qualifications (FSMQs); these are examined by OCR.

In partnership with Hodder Murray, MEI are responsible for three major series of textbooks: Formula One Maths for Key Stage 3, Hodder Mathematics for GCSE and the MEI Structured Mathematics series, including this book, for AS and A Level.

As well as textbooks, MEI take a leading role in the development of on-line resources to support mathematics. The books in this series are complemented by a major MEI website providing full solutions to the exercises, extra questions including on-line multiple choice tests, interactive demonstrations of the mathematics, schemes of work, and much more.

In recent years MEI have worked hard to promote Further Mathematics and, in conjunction with the DfES, they are now establishing the national network of Further Mathematics Centres.

MEI are committed to supporting the professional development of teachers. In addition to a programme of Continual Professional Development, MEI, in partnership with several universities, co-ordinate the Teaching Advanced Mathematics programme, a course designed to give teachers the skills and confidence to teach A Level mathematics successfully.

Much of the work of MEI is supported by the Gatsby Charitable Foundation. MEI is a registered charity and a charitable company. MEI's website and email addresses are **www.mei.org.uk** and **office@mei.org.uk**.

Introduction

This book has been written primarily to support the MEI Structured Mathematics module entitled Differential Equations. However it is also eminently suitable for use with any introductory course on differential equations in school, college or university. It is supported by additional on-line materials available through the MEI distance learning programme at *www.mei.org.uk*.

The study of differential equations is important for applied mathematicians, scientists and engineers because these equations provide mathematical models for the many real-world situations involving continuous change. Chapter 1 sets the scene by formulating differential equations for a wide range of situations. Subsequent chapters explore both theory and applications so that as well as learning how to do the mathematics you see its relevance and how to use it to express and solve real problems.

Chapters 2 to 5 explore the solutions of first order differential equations graphically, analytically and, in the case of Chapter 5, numerically. Chapters 6 to 8 deal with the solutions of second order differential equations and their application to oscillating systems. In these chapters you will need an understanding of some basic concepts in mechanics, in particular kinematics and Newton's laws of motion. Chapter 9 provides an introduction to the solution of systems of differential equations involving two or more dependent variables.

This is the third edition of *Differential Equations* in this series. It has been expanded to include new questions from more recent examination papers. Thanks are due to Peter Mitchell for his work in preparing the new edition. We would also like to express our appreciation to the many people who have helped with advice and suggestions during the development of earlier editions, in particular David Edsall, Mike Jones, John Reade, Judith Anstice and Diana Cowey. Finally we would also like to thank the various examination boards who have given permission for their past questions to be used in the exercises.

John Berry, Ted Graham, Peter Mitchell and Roger Porkess

Contents

Using differential equations in modelling

It isn't that they can't see the solution.
It is that they can't see the problem.

G.K. Chesterton

How does the quantity of a drug
in the body vary with time?

How long does a cup of
coffee take to cool?

After how many days will the
moon take this shape again?

Each of these problems involves quantities that are continuously changing. If you think for a moment you will realise that there are many situations in which this is the case. We observe change in everything we see. Some of these changes are permanent: the coffee will cool to the temperature of the surroundings and then stay at that temperature. Some changes are cyclic: the shape of the moon in the sky follows a cyclic pattern.

The area of mathematics that describes quantities that change continuously is called *calculus*. The rate of change of a quantity is called its *derivative*, and equations that involve the derivative are called *differential equations*.

At its simplest, a differential equation provides information about the rate of change of one variable with respect to another in terms of those variables, for example

$$\frac{dy}{dx} = x + y, \quad \frac{dP}{dt} = 0.02P$$

The *solution* of a differential equation provides a relationship between the variables themselves and does not involve derivatives. For these two equations the solutions are $y = -x - 1 + ce^x$ and $P = P_0 e^{0.02t}$ (where c and P_0 are constants). More complicated differential equations may involve higher derivatives e.g. $\dfrac{d^2s}{dt^2}, \dfrac{d^3y}{dx^3}$, or further variables.

Modelling with differential equations

The process of using mathematics to solve problems in the real world is called *mathematical modelling*. It is described by the flowchart in figure 1.1.

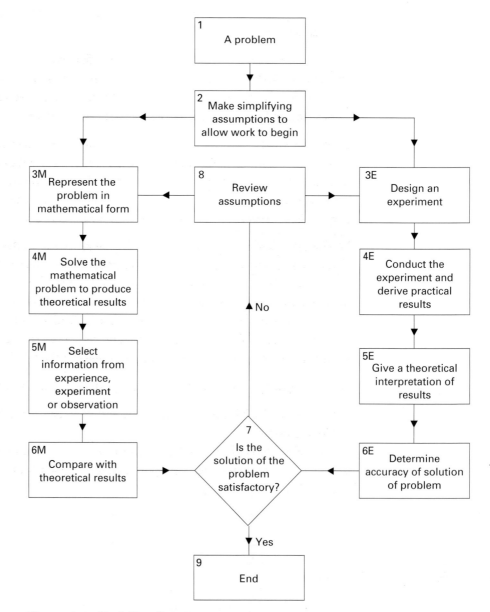

Figure 1.1 *Modelling flowchart*

In order to solve a problem successfully you need to find a mathematical model that describes the situation adequately. This model could take the form of an inequality, an equation or an algorithm (a set of steps). In this book you will meet problems for which the most appropriate model is a differential equation.

With many problems you will be able to go straight into the mathematics (the left-hand cycle of the flowchart). This will usually be the case if the problem can be solved by applying models which are familiar to you. Most problems in mechanics are of this sort, because their solution involves the use of well-established models, such as Newton's laws of motion. Your solution to a problem will depend on the assumptions and simplications you have made, so it may not be correct even if your calculations are sound. Even when you are solving a problem using modelling rather than experimental methods, you need some data to check your answer.

On the other hand, if no model is available, the first work you do after making your assumptions will be experimental (the right-hand side of the flowchart). This should help you to understand the problem better, give you some figures to work with and help you to formulate a mathematical model.

To see how the modelling cycle works, we shall use it to analyse a medical problem. Caffeine is a stimulatory drug present in many drinks including coffee, tea and cola. It is known that too much caffeine in the body can be a health hazard. Suppose you are asked to predict the amount of caffeine remaining in a person's body some given interval after drinking a cup of strong coffee.

The first step is to understand the physiological processes involved in the situation, and to make simplifying assumptions to allow you to begin work on the problem (box 2 of the flowchart). The process of removing a drug from the human body varies with the drug. It involves a variety of organs, the most important of which are the kidneys. Removal of a drug by the kidneys (called 'renal clearance') releases the drug via the bladder into the urine. The rate of renal clearance of a drug can be measured by testing samples of urine.

You can begin by making the following simplifications and assumptions.

1 Once the coffee has been drunk, the caffeine is instantly absorbed into the bloodstream.
2 The caffeine is cleared from the bloodstream by renal clearance.
3 The rate of renal clearance is proportional to the quantity of the drug in the body.

Now you can formulate a mathematical model. If you let t represent time (in hours) and q represent the quantity (in mg) of caffeine present in the body tissues, statement 3 above can be written as:

$$\frac{dq}{dt} \propto q$$

or

$$\frac{dq}{dt} = -kq.$$

k is a positive constant, the constant of proportionality.

You introduce a negative sign because you know the quantity of caffeine decreases with time.

This is an example of a differential equation. You will see later that its solution is given by

$$q = Ae^{-kt},$$

where A is a constant, the constant of integration. Although you could not yet have arrived at this solution for yourself, you can check that it is a solution of the differential equation by differentiating both sides:

$$\frac{dq}{dt} = A(-ke^{-kt}) = -kq.$$

So if $q = Ae^{-kt}$, then q satisfies the differential equation $\frac{dq}{dt} = -kq$.

The next step is to use information from experiments to find values of A and k. Suppose you have the following experimental results.

1 A cup of strong coffee contains 150 mg of caffeine.
2 The amount of caffeine cleared from the body in any one-hour period is approximately 25% of the amount present at the start of the hour.

Substituting the data from result 1 into the equation for q:
when $t = 0$, $q = 150$, so

$$150 = Ae^0 = A.$$

So in this case the constant of integration, A, is 150. Our equation for q is now

$$q = 150e^{-kt}.$$

Substituting the data from result 2 into this equation:

when $t = 1$, $q = \frac{75}{100} \times 150 = 112.5$, so

$$112.5 = 150e^{-k}.$$

Dividing both sides by 150 and then taking logarithms gives the constant of proportionality as

$$k = -\ln\left(\frac{112.5}{150}\right) = 0.288 \quad \text{(correct to 3 significant figures).}$$

Based on the assumptions, simplifications and given data, the amount of caffeine at time t is given by

$$q = 150e^{-0.288t}.$$

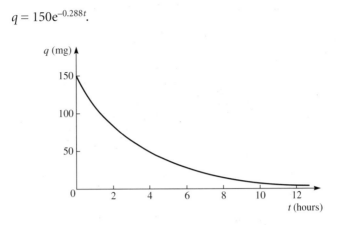

Figure 1.2 *Graph of quantity of caffeine in body against time*

This equation gives the amount of caffeine in the body as a function of time. It is a mathematical model formulated using both the modelling and experimental cycles. Further experimental information, such as tests of caffeine levels against time, would be needed to validate the model (box 6E of the modelling flowchart). For any real problem, you should expect to go round one or both cycles of the chart at least twice and possibly several times before you home in on a model that not only looks good on paper but actually matches the real world.

? 1 How is the rate of cooling of a cup of coffee related to its current temperature?
2 How is the rate of growth of a population related to its current size?
3 A chemical has spilled into a reservoir causing unsafe levels of pollution. Fresh water is fed into the reservoir from a river, and water is drained from the reservoir at the same rate. How does the concentration of the chemical in the reservoir change with time?

INVESTIGATION

Use the model derived in the text, $q = 150e^{-0.288t}$, to help you answer these questions.

1 Calculate the approximate time taken for 50% of the caffeine to be eliminated from the body.
2 According to this model, after one cup of strong coffee the amount of caffeine in the body never again reaches zero. Do you think this is realistic?
3 Investigate the possibility of receiving a convulsive dose (10 g) of caffeine by drinking strong coffee, one cup at a time, at equal time intervals. (The convulsive dose is the dose which can cause death.)

Forming differential equations from rates of change

If you are given sufficient information about the rate of change of a quantity, such as the caffeine level in the body or the height of water in a harbour, you can form a differential equation to model the situation. It is important to look carefully at the problem before writing down an equivalent mathematical statement. You have to decide whether you need a model for a rate of change with respect to time or with respect to another variable such as distance or height. You need to be familiar with the language used in these different cases.

If the altitude, h, of an aircraft is being considered, the phrase *rate of change of altitude* might be used. This actually means the *rate of change of altitude with respect to time*. You could write it as $\dfrac{dh}{dt}$ where t stands for time. However, you might be more interested in how the altitude of the aircraft changes with the horizontal distance it has travelled. In this case you would talk about *the rate of change of altitude with respect to horizontal distance*, and you could write it as $\dfrac{dh}{dx}$ where x stands for the horizontal distance travelled.

You should be aware of two shorthand notations. Differentiation with respect to time is often indicated by writing a dot above the variable, for example $\dfrac{dx}{dt}$ may be written as $\dot{x}$, $\dfrac{d^2y}{dt^2}$ as $\ddot{y}$. (You say these as 'x dot' and 'y double dot'.)

Differentiation with respect to x may be denoted by the use of the symbol ', so that y' means $\dfrac{dy}{dx}$, f'' means $\dfrac{d^2f}{dx^2}$. (You say these as 'y dash' and 'f double dash'.)

Any equation which involves a derivative such as $\dfrac{dq}{dt}$, $\dfrac{dy}{dx}$ or $\dfrac{d^2x}{dt^2}$ is called a differential equation. A differential equation which involves a first derivative such as $\dfrac{dq}{dt}$ is called a *first order differential equation*. One which involves a second order derivative such as $\dfrac{d^2x}{dt^2}$ is called a *second order differential equation*.

A third order differential equation involves a third order derivative, and so on.

The following examples show how differential equations can be formed from descriptions of a wide variety of situations.

EXAMPLE 1.1

The population of a country increases at a rate that is proportional to its present population. When the population is 50 million it is increasing at a rate of 2 million per year. Use this information to find a differential equation for the rate of change of the population.

SOLUTION

With variables t (for time in years) and P (for population in millions), the rate of increase of the population is written as $\dfrac{dP}{dt}$. The rate of increase is proportional to the current population, P, so you can write

$$\frac{dP}{dt} = kP$$

where k is the positive constant of proportionality.

You are also told that when $P = 50$, $\dfrac{dP}{dt} = 2$. You can substitute these values into the differential equation to find the value of k:

$$2 = k \times 50$$
$$k = \frac{1}{25}$$

So the differential equation is $\dfrac{dP}{dt} = \dfrac{P}{25}$.

> This is the rate of increase of population measured in millions per year.

EXAMPLE 1.2

Newton's law of cooling states that the rate at which a body cools is proportional to the difference between its temperature and the temperature of the surrounding air. Initially a kettle has a temperature of 100°C and is cooling at a rate of 2°C min^{-1}; the surrounding air has a temperature of 20°C. Use this information to find an expression for $\dfrac{dT}{dt}$, where T is the temperature of the kettle in °C.

SOLUTION

According to Newton's law of cooling, the rate of cooling is proportional to the temperature difference between the kettle and the air. In this case you can write

$$\frac{dT}{dt} = -k(T - 20).$$

> You know the temperature is decreasing. If you put a minus sign here you expect k to be positive. The minus sign could be omitted and in that case k would be negative.

When $T = 100$, $\dfrac{dT}{dt} = -2$, so

$$-2 = -k(100 - 20)$$
$$k = \frac{2}{80} = \frac{1}{40}.$$

The equation is therefore

$$\frac{dT}{dt} = -\frac{1}{40}(T - 20).$$

EXAMPLE 1.3

A simple model of the atmosphere above the Earth's surface is as a perfect gas at constant temperature. This means that

- the pressure, p, at any point is proportional to the density, ρ

- the rate at which the pressure decreases with height, z, is proportional to the density.

Use this information to find an expression for $\dfrac{dp}{dz}$ in terms of p.

SOLUTION

Since the pressure, p, at any point is proportional to the density at that point, you can write

$$p = c_1\,\rho,$$

where c_1 is a positive constant.

Since the rate of change of pressure, p, with height, z, is proportional to the density, ρ, you can write

$$\frac{dp}{dz} = -c_2\,\rho,$$

Negative sign introduced because pressure decreases with height.

where c_2 is a positive constant.

Substituting for ρ from the first equation into the second gives

$$\frac{dp}{dz} = -\frac{c_2}{c_1}p = -cp.$$

c is a constant formed from c_1 and c_2

EXAMPLE 1.4

A parachutist and her equipment have a combined mass of $70\,\text{kg}$ and a terminal speed of $5\,\text{ms}^{-1}$. Using the modelling assumption that the air resistance $R\,\text{N}$ is proportional to the speed $v\,\text{ms}^{-1}$ of the parachutist, find an expression for $\dfrac{dv}{dt}$ at time t seconds. (Take g to be $10\,\text{ms}^{-2}$.)

SOLUTION

Figure 1.3 shows the forces acting on a parachutist of mass m. The force mg is the force of gravity acting vertically downwards, and R is the air resistance. You assume that the parachutist falls vertically in a straight line, and you take distances and speeds as positive in the downward direction.

Figure 1.3

As well as using the information given, you need to use an established mathematical model, Newton's second law, to link the motion of the parachutist to the forces acting on her.

The resultant downward force is $mg - R$.

Applying Newton's second law, $F = ma$, at any instant gives

$$mg - R = m\frac{dv}{dt}.$$

This side is F in $F = ma$.

$\frac{dv}{dt}$ is the acceleration at that instant.

Dividing both sides by m gives

$$g - \frac{R}{m} = \frac{dv}{dt}.$$

The modelling assumption that R is proportional to v gives $R = kv$ and so

$$\frac{dv}{dt} = g - \frac{kv}{m}.$$

This is the differential equation of motion for a parachutist of unknown mass. In this case the parachutist has mass $70\,\text{kg}$ and reaches a terminal speed of $5\,\text{ms}^{-1}$, and you can use these values to calculate k.

At the terminal speed the acceleration is zero, i.e.

$$\frac{dv}{dt} = 0.$$

You can therefore write $g - \frac{kv}{m} = 0$.

Taking $g = 10$ and substituting $m = 70$ and $v = 5$ gives

$$10 - \frac{5k}{70} = 0$$

so $\quad k = \frac{700}{5} = 140.$

Substituting for k in the expression for $\frac{dv}{dt}$ gives

$$\frac{dv}{dt} = 10 - \frac{140}{70}v = 10 - 2v.$$

This is the differential equation of motion for this particular parachute jump.

EXAMPLE 1.5

The volume, V, of a spherical raindrop of radius r is decreasing (due to evaporation) at a rate proportional to its surface area, S. Find an expression for $\frac{dr}{dt}$.

SOLUTION

Note that the problem description contains four variables, V, S, r and t, but that V and S are themselves functions of the radius r:

$$V = \tfrac{4}{3}\pi r^3 \quad \text{and} \quad S = 4\pi r^2.$$

You can use this to write the problem more simply in terms of the two variables, r and t.

The wording of the problem gives

$$\frac{dV}{dt} = -kS = -k(4\pi r^2)$$

where k is a positive constant. The next step is to write this equation in terms of r. The left-hand side of the differential equation may be rewritten using the chain rule in the form

$$\frac{dV}{dt} = \frac{dV}{dr} \times \frac{dr}{dt}.$$

Since $V = \tfrac{4}{3}\pi r^3$, $\quad \dfrac{dV}{dr} = 4\pi r^2.$

So $\quad \dfrac{dV}{dt} = 4\pi r^2 \times \dfrac{dr}{dt}.$

The differential equation is now written

$$4\pi r^2 \frac{dr}{dt} = -4k\pi r^2$$

$$\Rightarrow \qquad \frac{dr}{dt} = -k.$$

This very simple differential equation tells you that the radius decreases at a constant rate. You can solve this equation directly, by integration.

EXERCISE 1A

1 During the decay of a radioactive substance, the rate at which mass is lost is proportional to the mass present at that instant. Write down a differential equation to describe this relationship.

2 In an electrical circuit, the voltage is decreasing at a rate proportional to the square of the present voltage. When the voltage is 20 volts it is decreasing at a rate of 1 Vs^{-1}. Form a differential equation to describe the rate of change of voltage with time.

3 The rate at which the population of a particular country increases is proportional to its population. Currently the population is 68 million, and it is increasing at a rate of 2 million per year. Form a differential equation for P, the population of the country in millions.

4 The population of a colony of rabbits increases at a rate proportional to the population. When the population is 30 rabbits, it is increasing at a rate of 5 rabbits per month. Form a differential equation to model this situation.

5 The rate at which water leaves a tank is modelled as being proportional to the square root of the height of water in the tank. Initially the height of water is 100 cm and water is leaving at the rate of 20 cm³ per second. Form a differential equation that describes this model.

6 A disease spreads so that the rate at which people are infected is proportional to the square root of the number already infected. When 100 people are known to be infected, new cases are appearing at a rate of 20 per day.

Find an expression for $\dfrac{dN}{dt}$.

7 After a drug has been injected into the bloodstream, its concentration gradually decreases and the drug loses effectiveness. Assume that the decrease in concentration is proportional to the present concentration. Form a differential equation to model this situation, given that the concentration is decreasing by 0.02 gcm⁻³ s⁻¹ when the concentration is 0.1 gcm⁻³.

8 A hot object cools according to Newton's law of cooling. Initially it has a temperature of 80°C and is cooling at a rate of 0.5°Cs⁻¹. The surrounding air has a temperature of 20°C. Form a differential equation to describe the temperature loss.

9 The area of a circle is increasing at a rate proportional to its radius.

(i) Write down an expression for $\dfrac{dA}{dt}$.

(ii) Find an expression for $\dfrac{dA}{dr}$ in terms of r.

(iii) Find an expression for $\dfrac{dr}{dt}$.

10 Air is escaping from a spherical balloon at a rate proportional to its surface area. Given that the air is escaping at 4 cm³s⁻¹ when the radius is 10 cm, find an expression for the rate of change of the radius, $\dfrac{dr}{dt}$.

11 A poker of length 1 m has one end in a fire. The temperature at each point of the poker remains the same at all times. However the temperature decreases along the length of the poker at a rate proportional to the distance from the hot end. A quarter of the way along the poker (from the hot end) the rate of decrease of the temperature is 16°C per centimetre. Formulate a differential equation to model this situation.

12 The water pressure in the sea increases with depth. At depth h below the surface, the rate of pressure increase with respect to depth is proportional to the density of sea water. The constant of proportionality is the acceleration due to gravity, g (9.8 ms⁻²).

The density ρ (in kg m⁻³) of sea water in part of an ocean is modelled by

$$\rho = 1000\,(1 + 0.001h) \quad 0 \leqslant h \leqslant 100$$
$$\rho = 1100 \quad\quad\quad\quad\quad h > 100$$

Find a differential equation to model this situation.

13 Heat-seeking missiles are designed to follow any object that emits heat. For example, an anti-aircraft missile can be 'locked on' to the heat of the exhaust from a jet engine, so that the missile always points towards the engine. This makes it harder for the aircraft to escape the missile by changing direction.

A heat-seeking missile is fired at an aircraft that is flying horizontally with constant speed v at a constant height of b. At the instant the missile is launched, the aircraft has co-ordinates (a, b) relative to the launch pad. At time t, the missile has position (x, y).

Formulate a differential equation for $\dfrac{dy}{dx}$, in terms of x, y and t, to model the path of the missile as it travels to intercept the aircraft.

14 Water is pumped into a conical tank at a rate of $0.3\,\text{m}^3$ per second. The tank has the dimensions shown in the diagram, and the depth of the water is h metres at time t seconds.

Find an expression for $\dfrac{dh}{dt}$

.

15 A volume V of water is held in a tank that has a square base, side $2\,\text{m}$, and height $4\,\text{m}$. Initially the tank is full. Water leaves the tank through a hole at the bottom at a rate of $\sqrt{20h}$ litres per second, where h is the depth of water in the tank. Find expressions for $\dfrac{dV}{dt}$ and $\dfrac{dh}{dt}$ in terms of h.

16 A can of drink is removed from a refrigerator, where it had a temperature of 2°C, and placed in a warm room which is at a temperature of 22°C. Form a differential equation that describes how the can warms up.

Constants of integration

The caffeine clearance problem (see page 3) is modelled by the first order differential equation

$$\frac{dq}{dt} = -kq,$$

and the constant of proportionality, k, has the value 0.288. Finding an expression for q is called *solving the differential equation*. In this case, the solution is

$$q = Ae^{-0.288t}.$$

This solution contains an unknown constant, A.

Some differential equations may be solved by direct integration. As you know, every time you integrate an expression, a constant of integration is produced. So when you solve a first order differential equation by direct integration you will end up with an expression that contains one constant of integration. If you solve a second order equation by direct integration, you end up with an expression that contains two constants of integration.

The same applies when you use other methods of solution: the solution of a first order differential equation contains one constant of integration, that of a second order equation contains two constants of integration, and so on.

The solution that contains these constants is called the *general solution* of the differential equation. Since it contains unknown constants, the general solution is actually a family of solutions, and it can be represented as a family of curves. For example, look at the differential equation

$$\frac{dy}{dx} = 2x - 1.$$

Integrating both sides with respect to x,

$$y = \int (2x - 1)\, dx$$
$$= x^2 - x + c$$

This is the general solution. Each value of c gives a different solution, and a different curve.

where c is the constant of integration.

Some members of the family of solutions of this differential equation are shown in figure 1.4.

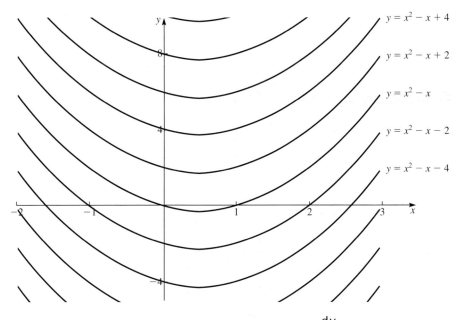

Figure 1.4 *Some solutions of the differential equation* $\frac{dy}{dx} = 2x - 1$.

Suppose that you are now given one extra piece of information, such as '$y = 2$ when $x = 3$'. You can use this information to find the particular value of c, and therefore the particular curve, that fits your problem.

Substituting $y = 2$ and $x = 3$ into the general solution gives

$$2 = 3^2 - 3 + c$$

and so $c = -4$.

The solution which fits your problem is

$$y = x^2 - x - 4.$$

This is a *particular solution* of the differential equation. It is represented in figure 1.4 by the curve which passes through $(0, -4)$. Now that you have identified a particular solution, you can find the value of y for any given value of x.

The extra piece of information that allows you to identify the particular solution for your problem is called a *condition*. It effectively gives you the co-ordinates of one of the points through which the required solution curve passes. In the case of a second order differential equation, the general solution contains two constants of integration, and so two conditions are needed to find a particular solution. For a third order differential equation, three conditions are needed, and so on.

Verification of solutions

You will meet situations in which you think you know the solution of a differential equation without actually having to solve it. It may be that the situation, or one like it, is familiar to you, or you may have experimental data that suggest a solution. In such situations you need to check or *verify* that your solution does indeed satisfy the differential equation. You do this by substituting the solution into the differential equation, a process called *verification*. Verification is also helpful in cases where you have found a solution but just want to check your working.

EXAMPLE 1.6

Verify that $y = Ae^{-3x}$ is the general solution of the differential equation

$$\frac{dy}{dx} = -3y$$

where A is a constant. Sketch some members of the family of solutions.

SOLUTION

Differentiating $y = Ae^{-3x}$ gives

$$\begin{aligned}\frac{dy}{dx} &= -3Ae^{-3x}\\ &= -3(Ae^{-3x})\\ &= -3y,\end{aligned}$$

so $y = Ae^{-3x}$ is a solution of the differential equation $\frac{dy}{dx} = -3y$.

Since each value of A leads to a different solution curve, this is the general solution of the differential equation. Some members of the family of solutions are shown in figure 1.5. The curves all have equation $y = Ae^{-3x}$, but each has a different value of A.

Note

If you are verifying a particular solution of a differential equation, you need to check

• that the expression satisfies the differential equation
• that it satisfies the given conditions.

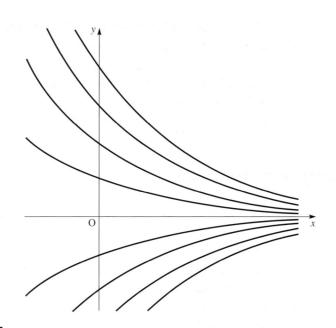

Figure 1.5

EXAMPLE 1.7

Verify that

$$v = 20e^{-2t} + 5$$

is the particular solution of the differential equation

$$\frac{dv}{dt} = 10 - 2v$$

that satisfies the condition $v = 25$ when $t = 0$.

SOLUTION

Differentiating $v = 20e^{-2t} + 5$ gives

$$\frac{dv}{dt} = -40e^{-2t}.$$

The right-hand side of the differential equation is $10 - 2v$. In this case,

$$10 - 2v = 10 - 2(20e^{-2t} + 5)$$
$$= 10 - 40e^{-2t} - 10$$
$$= -40e^{-2t}$$
$$= \frac{dv}{dt}.$$

This is the given expression for v

So the solution $v = 20e^{-2t} + 5$ satisfies the differential equation

$$\frac{dv}{dt} = 10 - 2v.$$

Since the expression for v contains no unknown constants, it is a particular solution of the differential equation. We must now check that it satisfies the given condition, so we substitute $t = 0$ into the expression:

when $t = 0$, $v = 20e^0 + 5 = 25$ as required.

So $v = 20e^{-2t} + 5$ is the particular solution of the differential equation that satisfies the condition that $v = 25$ when $t = 0$.

EXERCISE 1B

1 Verify that $P = 40e^{0.2t}$ is a solution of

$$\frac{dP}{dt} = \frac{P}{5}.$$

2 Verify that $M = 10e^{-5t}$ is a solution of

$$\frac{dM}{dt} = -5M.$$

3 (i) Verify that $v = 20(1 - e^{-0.5t})$ is a solution of the differential equation

$$\frac{dv}{dt} = 10 - 0.5v.$$

(ii) What is the value of v when $t = 0$?

(iii) What happens to v for large values of t?

4 The temperature, T, of an object changes such that

$$\frac{dT}{dt} = 2 - 0.1T.$$

(i) Verify that $T = 20 + 60e^{-0.1t}$ is a solution of this differential equation.

(ii) Verify that $T = 20 - 18e^{-0.1t}$ is also a solution.

(iii) One of the solutions above models the temperature change of a cup of coffee placed in a room, and the other models that of a cold carton of juice just taken from a fridge. Which solution corresponds to which object?

5 A population grows so that

$$\frac{dP}{dt} = \frac{P}{20}.$$

(i) Verify that $P = Ce^{\frac{t}{20}}$ is the general solution of this equation.

(ii) When $t = 0$ the population is 50. Find the particular solution in this case.

(iii) Write down the particular solution corresponding to an initial population of 100.

(iv) Sketch a number of curves to illustrate the family of solutions.

6 A radioactive substance decays so that its mass, m mg, decreases according to the equation

$$\frac{dm}{dt} = -\frac{m}{100}$$

where the time t is measured in hours.

(i) Verify that $m = 20e^{-\frac{t}{100}}$ is a solution of this differential equation.

(ii) Find the half-life (time taken for the mass to halve) for this substance.

(iii) What is the initial mass of the substance?

(iv) Write down the solution that would apply if the initial mass were 50 mg.

7 Verify that $y = \dfrac{-2}{x^2 + 2}$ is the solution of the differential equation

$$\frac{dy}{dx} = xy^2$$

that satisfies the initial condition $y = -1$ when $x = 0$.

8 By integrating both sides find the general solution of the differential equation

$$\frac{dy}{dx} = 3x^2 - x + 1.$$

Find the particular solution that satisfies the condition $y = 4$ when $x = 1$.

Sketch a number of curves to illustrate the family of solutions including the particular solution that passes through the point $(1, 4)$.

9 Find the general solution of the differential equation

$$\frac{ds}{dt} = 4 - 10t.$$

Find the particular solution that satisfies the initial condition $s = 11$ when $t = 0$.

10 Which of the following are possible solutions of the differential equation

$$\frac{dy}{dx} = -8y?$$

A $y = 4e^{-8x}$ **B** $y = 8e^{-4x}$

C $y = 4e^{-8x} + 2$ **D** $y = 4e^{-8x} + 8$

E $y = 8e^{-8x}$

11 **(i)** Verify that $P = P_0 e^{k(t-t_0)}$ is a solution of the differential equation

$$\frac{dP}{dt} = kP.$$

(ii) Verify that $P = Ae^{kt}$ is also a solution of the differential equation.

(iii) Express A in terms of k, t_0 and P_0.

12 **(i)** Verify that $T = \alpha + Ae^{-kt}$ is a solution of the differential equation

$$\frac{dT}{dt} = -k(T - \alpha) \quad (k > 0)$$

which models Newton's law of cooling.

(ii) Find, in terms of A and α, the initial and final temperatures of the object.

(iii) An object at a temperature of 90°C is placed in a room at 25°C. State the values of α and A in this case.

(iv) Sketch this family of curves including cases when A is both positive and negative.

13 The acceleration of a stone sliding down a slope submerged in a fluid can be modelled as

$$\frac{dv}{dt} = 4 - v.$$

(i) Show that $v = Ae^{-t} + 4$ satisfies the differential equation.

(ii) Determine the value of A if the initial speed of the stone is $8\,\text{ms}^{-1}$.

14 Show that $y = Ae^x - (x^2 + 2x + 2)$ is a solution of the differential equation

$$\frac{dy}{dx} = y + x^2.$$

15 In a model (which applies up to heights of about 10 km) for the pressure p in the lower atmosphere at a height z metres above sea level, it is assumed that gravity is constant and that the air behaves as a perfect gas. This gives the differential equation

$$\frac{dp}{dz} = -\frac{pg}{RT}$$

where g is the acceleration due to gravity, R is the universal gas constant and T is the absolute temperature of the air in Kelvin (K). The value of R is $8.314\,\text{JK}^{-1}\,\text{mol}^{-1}$.

The temperature distribution in the lower atmosphere is given by

$$T = 300 - 0.006z$$

(i) Taking g to be $10\,\text{ms}^{-2}$, show that this differential equation may, to good approximation, be written

$$\frac{1}{p}\frac{dp}{dz} = -\frac{200}{(50\,000 - z)}$$

(ii) Show that

$$p = p_0 \left(1 - \frac{z}{50\,000}\right)^{200}$$

satisfies this differential equation, given that $p = p_0$ when $z = 0$.

1 A differential equation is an equation involving derivatives such as

$$\frac{dy}{dx}, \frac{dV}{dt} \text{ or } \frac{d^2x}{dt^2}.$$

2 The order of a differential equation is the order of its highest derivative.

3 Differential equations are used to model situations which involve rates of change.

4 The solution of a differential equation gives the relationship between the variables themselves, not their derivatives.

5 The general solution of a first order differential equation satisfies the differential equation and has one constant of integration in the solution.

6 A particular solution of a differential equation is one in which additional information has been used to calculate the constant of integration.

7 The general solution may be represented by a family of curves and a particular solution is one member of that family.

8 To verify that a function is a particular solution you must check that the function satisfies both the given differential equation and the initial conditions.

Tangent fields

He ... flung himself upon his horse and rode off madly in all directions.

Stephen Leacock

A shoal of fish can behave as if it were a single organism, displaying an ever-changing pattern of curves. At any instant, the body of each fish forms the tangent to one of the curves in the pattern.

The curves in a magnetic field (shown by the iron filings in the photo), indicate the direction of the magnetic force at any point.

In Chapter 1 you saw the solutions of differential equations represented graphically. The graphs were drawn using the algebraic, or *analytical*, form of the solutions. For many differential equations you cannot find an analytical solution. But even in these cases you can still predict the behaviour of the variables using graphical techniques, and this chapter shows you how to do so.

A differential equation gives you information about the rate of change of the dependent variable but not about the actual value of the variable at any instant. The information about the rate of change can be represented graphically as a *tangent field* (sometimes called a *direction field*), and this can be used to sketch approximate solution curves for the differential equation.

To see how this works, look again at the caffeine clearance problem of Chapter 1.

The differential equation modelling the situation is

$$\frac{\mathrm{d}q}{\mathrm{d}t} = -0.288q.$$

For any value of q you can use this to calculate $\dfrac{dq}{dt}$. For example, if $q = 150$, $\dfrac{dq}{dt} = -43.2$. So you know that when q has the value 150, whatever the value of t, the gradient of the solution curve is -43.2. You can represent this on a graph of q against t by drawing short dashes with gradient -43.2 at $q = 150$. (When working out the angle at which the lines should be drawn you will need to take into account the scales on your axes.) You can repeat this process for other values of q, until you have built up a tangent field for the differential equation, as shown in figure 2.1.

As you have seen, the general solution of a first order differential equation can be represented by a family of curves. Each curve represents one particular solution. For example, in the caffeine clearance problem you were interested in the particular solution corresponding to $q = 150$ when $t = 0$. Using the tangent field, you could sketch this curve, starting at the point (0, 150) and using the direction indicators as a guide. This has been done in figure 2.2. Curves have been sketched also for two different initial caffeine concentrations, $q = 100$ and $q = 50$. These represent two other particular solutions of the differential equation. You can see that any particular solution of the differential equation could be sketched in this way.

Figure 2.1

Figure 2.2

For the caffeine clearance problem you know the analytical solution:

$$q = Ae^{-0.288t}.$$

This means that you can calculate an accurate value for q at any time t. However, when an analytical solution is not available, or has a complicated form, you can use a tangent field to find approximate values, and to gain an understanding of the behaviour of the variable(s) in question.

EXAMPLE 2.1

For the differential equation $\dfrac{dy}{dx} = x^2 + y^2$,

(i) set up a table of values giving $\dfrac{dy}{dx}$ for integer values of x and y, for

$-2 \leqslant x \leqslant 2$ and $-2 \leqslant y \leqslant 2$

(ii) use the values in your table to draw the tangent field in the region covered by the table

(iii) sketch the solution curve which passes through the point $(0, 1)$.

SOLUTION

(i)

y \\ x	−2	−1	0	1	2
2	8	5	4	5	8
1	5	2	1	2	5
0	4	1	0	1	4
−1	5	2	1	2	5
−2	8	5	4	5	8

(ii) and **(iii)**

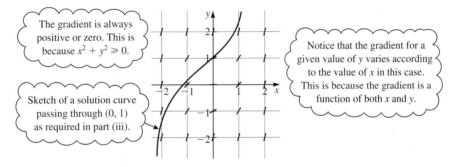

The gradient is always positive or zero. This is because $x^2 + y^2 \geqslant 0$.

Sketch of a solution curve passing through $(0, 1)$ as required in part (iii).

Notice that the gradient for a given value of y varies according to the value of x in this case. This is because the gradient is a function of both x and y.

Figure 2.3

Drawing tangent fields by hand can be very time-consuming. Many computer packages include a facility for drawing them, and this saves time; some of the tangent fields in this book are computer-generated. It is often useful, though, to look at the curves along which the direction indicators have the same gradient. These curves are called the *isoclines*, and they can be useful whether you are drawing the tangent field by hand or interpreting a computer display.

For the differential equation $\dfrac{dy}{dx} = 2y$, $\dfrac{dy}{dx}$ has the same value, namely 8, at the points $(-2, 4)$, $(0, 4)$, $(1, 4)$, $(4, 4)$. The line $y = 4$ is an isocline. In this example, all the lines parallel to the x axis are isoclines (figure 2.4).

Figure 2.4 *Isoclines for* $\dfrac{dy}{dx} = 2y$

For the differential equation in the previous example, $\dfrac{dy}{dx} = x^2 + y^2$, the isocline for points where $\dfrac{dy}{dx}$ has value m is the circle $x^2 + y^2 = m$. This has centre the origin and radius $\sqrt{m}$ (figure 2.5).

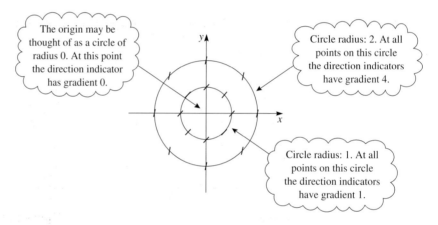

The origin may be thought of as a circle of radius 0. At this point the direction indicator has gradient 0.

Circle radius: 2. At all points on this circle the direction indicators have gradient 4.

Circle radius: 1. At all points on this circle the direction indicators have gradient 1.

Figure 2.5 *Isoclines for* $\dfrac{dy}{dx} = x^2 + y^2$

Information from the isoclines can often save a lot of work in drawing the tangent field. Having drawn the isoclines, it is then a simple matter to draw in as many direction indicators as you need to make the family of curves become clear.

Notice that for the differential equation $\dfrac{dy}{dx} = x^2 + y^2$, no analytical solution is possible. The use of tangent fields has allowed you nonetheless to learn a great deal about the solution curves. Since many differential equations do not have analytical solutions, tangent fields provide a useful and powerful method.

In the next example the differential equation is one which can be solved analytically, but drawing the tangent field allows you to deduce the main features of the situation which it is modelling, without finding the analytical solution.

EXAMPLE 2.2

The differential equation $\dfrac{dv}{dt} = 10 - 5v$ models the velocity of an object falling through a liquid.

(i) Sketch the tangent field for $0 \leqslant t \leqslant 2$ and $0 \leqslant v \leqslant 4$.

(ii) Superimpose the solution curves which represent an object that is initially

    (a) at rest

    (b) moving at $4\,\text{ms}^{-1}$.

(iii) From the tangent field deduce the terminal speed of the object.

SOLUTION

(i) The table gives the values of $\dfrac{dv}{dt}$ for different values of v. (Note that in this case $\dfrac{dv}{dt}$ depends only on v and not on t.)

v	0	1	2	3	4
$\dfrac{dv}{dt}$	10	5	0	−5	−10

The values of the gradient $\dfrac{dv}{dt}$ become direction indicators in the tangent field.

These are plotted in figure 2.6.

Figure 2.6   **Figure 2.7**

(ii) To superimpose a solution curve, you select the starting point and draw a curve from the point such that its gradient is always the same as that shown by the direction indicators. Figure 2.7 shows the curves for initial speeds of 0 and $4\,\text{ms}^{-1}$.

(iii) The tangent field shows that as t increases all the solution curves approach the horizontal line $v = 2$. When $v = 2$, $\dfrac{dv}{dt}$ becomes zero and the speed does not change, so $v = 2$ is the terminal speed. (Notice how quickly the terminal speed is approached in both of the cases illustrated.)

1 (i) Copy and complete the table below, giving the values of $\dfrac{dy}{dx}$ where $\dfrac{dy}{dx} = 2x$.

y \ x	−2	−1	0	1	2
2					
1					
0					
−1					
−2					

(ii) Sketch the tangent field.

(iii) Sketch the particular solutions that pass through $(0, 2)$, $(1, 0)$ and $(0, 0)$.

(iv) Find the general solution of this differential equation analytically.

(v) Find the equations of the three curves you drew in part (iii).

(vi) Describe the isoclines for the tangent field you drew in part (ii).

2 (i) Construct a table for integer values of x and y from −2 to 2 giving the values of $\dfrac{dy}{dx}$ where $\dfrac{dy}{dx} = \dfrac{1-x}{y}$.

(ii) Sketch the tangent field.

(iii) Superimpose particular solutions that pass through $(0, 1)$, $(−1, 0)$ and $(0, 0)$.

(iv) Find the equation of the line joining the points at which the gradient is $\frac{1}{2}$.

(v) Describe the isoclines for the tangent field.

3 Given that $\dfrac{dy}{dx} = y$,

(i) describe the isoclines of the corresponding tangent field

(ii) draw the tangent field for $−3 \leqslant x \leqslant 3$ and $−3 \leqslant y \leqslant 3$

(iii) sketch the curves which pass through $(1, 2)$ and $(3, −3)$.

4 Given that $\dfrac{dy}{dx} = 4 - y$,

(i) describe the isoclines and give the equation of the isocline joining points at which the gradient is 3

(ii) draw the tangent field for $0 \leqslant x \leqslant 5$, $0 \leqslant y \leqslant 8$

(iii) sketch in the curves which pass through $(1, 2)$ and $(1, 6)$.

(iv) What do you notice about the two curves you have just sketched?

5 (i) Given that $\dfrac{dy}{dx} = 4 - 2y$, draw a tangent field for $0 \leqslant x \leqslant 4, 0 \leqslant y \leqslant 4$.

(ii) Superimpose solution curves that pass through $(0, 4)$ and $(0, 1)$.

6 (i) Copy and complete the diagram by marking in accurately the direction indicators at the points marked with dots, given that $\dfrac{dy}{dx} = \dfrac{y}{x}$

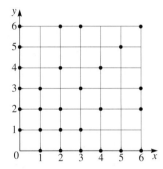

(ii) Give the equation of the isocline joining points at which the gradient is m (in the form $y = \ldots$).

(iii) Sketch in the curves which pass through the points

(a) $(5, 5)$ **(b)** $(4, 0)$ **(c)** $(0, 3)$
(d) $(6, 3)$ **(e)** $(2, 6)$

(iv) What do you notice about the five curves that you have just sketched? Use this information to draw the curve through the point $(4, 6)$.

(v) Why can't you mark in the direction indicator at the origin?

7 Given that $\dfrac{dy}{dx} = x + y$,

   (i) state the equation of the isocline joining points at which the gradient is m

   (ii) draw the tangent field for $-2 \leqslant x \leqslant 2$, $-2 \leqslant y \leqslant 2$

   (iii) on your diagram, draw the isocline which joins points at which the gradient is zero

   (iv) sketch in the curves which pass through

     (a) $(0, -1)$ **(b)** $(2, 2)$.

8 Given that $\dfrac{dy}{dx} = y - x$,

   (i) state the equation of the isocline joining points at which the gradient is m

   (ii) draw the tangent field for $-2 \leqslant x \leqslant 2$, $-2 \leqslant y \leqslant 2$

   (iii) on your diagram draw the isocline which joins points at which the gradient is zero

   (iv) sketch in the curves which pass through

     (a) $(1, 2)$ **(b)** $(2, -1)$.

9 Given that $\dfrac{dy}{dx} = xy$,

   (i) state the equation of the isocline joining points at which the gradient is m, and state the name given to this curve

   (ii) draw the tangent field for $-2 \leqslant x \leqslant 2$, $-2 \leqslant y \leqslant 2$

   (iii) describe the isocline which joins points at which the gradient is zero

   (iv) sketch in the curves which pass through

     (a) $(2, 2)$ **(b)** $(0, -1)$ **(c)** $(0, 0)$.

10 The rate of change of current in a circuit is modelled by $\dfrac{di}{dt} = 3 - i$.

   (i) Draw a tangent field for $0 \leqslant i \leqslant 4$ and $0 \leqslant t \leqslant 4$.

   (ii) Draw the solution curve that represents an initial current of 0.

   (iii) What is the current in the circuit after a long period of time?

11 A parachutist falls such that $\dfrac{dv}{dt} = 8 - v$ where $v\,\text{ms}^{-1}$ is the speed at time t s.

The diagram shows the tangent field for $0 \leqslant v \leqslant 10$ and $0 \leqslant t \leqslant 10$.

   (i) Sketch solution curves corresponding to initial speeds

     (a) $0\,\text{ms}^{-1}$ **(b)** $5\,\text{ms}^{-1}$ **(c)** $10\,\text{ms}^{-1}$

   (ii) What is the terminal speed in each of these cases?

12 The first order differential equation $y' = xy$ is being investigated. In order to gain some qualitative information about its solutions the tangent field is to be drawn using the following method, known as the *method of isoclines*. An isocline is a curve through points at which the solution curves have the same gradient. For example, the curve with equation $2 = xy$ is an isocline because it passes through all points on the solution curves where the gradient is 2. In general, the gradient y' is replaced by a parameter m, the specified gradient. The isoclines for this differential equation then have the form $m = xy$ (i.e. $y = \dfrac{m}{x}$). Short line elements with gradient m are drawn at intervals along each isocline with parameter m, thus producing the tangent field.

   (i) Using graph paper, sketch isoclines for $-4 \leqslant x \leqslant 4$ and $-4 \leqslant y \leqslant 4$ with values of the parameter m given by $m = 0, \pm\frac{1}{2}, \pm1, \pm2$ and ±4.

   (ii) Draw in the appropriate line elements of gradient m and hence produce the tangent field.

   (iii) Use the tangent field to sketch the solution curve of the differential equation $y' = xy$ which passes through the point $\left(0, \frac{1}{2}\right)$.

(iv) Solve the differential equation with the condition that $y = \frac{1}{2}$ when $x = 0$.

[**MEI**]

13 Both x and y are functions of t and satisfy the simultaneous differential equations

$$\frac{dx}{dt} = x + y, \quad \frac{dy}{dt} = 3y - x.$$

Before finding an analytic solution, a graphical description of the solution curves of y against x is obtained, using the tangent field method. By eliminating t from the above equations, we obtain $\dfrac{dy}{dx} = \dfrac{3y - x}{y + x}$.

(i) For any solution curve, write down the gradient at points where it crosses each of the co-ordinate axes, excluding the origin.

(ii) Find the equations of the straight lines on which the gradient of the solution curves is either zero or infinite.

(iii) Find the value of the constant m for which $y = mx$ is a solution of the differential equation.

(iv) By using the information you have found on a tangent field diagram, sketch the solution curve which passes through the point $(0, 1)$. On the same diagram sketch the three curves which represent solutions passing through *one* of the three points $(0, -1)$ and $(\pm, 0)$.

(v) Indicate by arrows the directions in which each of these solution curves is described as the parameter t increases.

[**MEI**]

14 The diagram describes the operation of a domestic air filter.

Air carrying dirt particles is drawn through the filter which removes the dirt but allows clean air to pass through. The equations which describe the motion of one such particle, at time t, are

$$\frac{du}{dt} = v - u, \quad \frac{dx}{dt} = -u$$

where u is the particle speed, v is the speed of the air and x is the displacement of the particle from the filter surface. This question concerns the case when the particle is close to the filter where v can be taken to be equal to $2x$.

(i) Use the information given to deduce that

$$\frac{du}{dx} = \frac{u - 2x}{u}.$$

We wish to draw a tangent field diagram for u against x, excluding the origin.

(ii) Write down the equation of the line in the u, x plane on which $\dfrac{du}{dx} = 0$.

(iii) Write down the values of the gradients at points on each of the co-ordinate axes.

(iv) Copy the diagram below and complete the tangent field at the missing points. Hence sketch the solution curves through the three points on the x axis where $x = 1$, 2 and 3.

Use the equation $\dfrac{dx}{dt} = -u$ to determine whether x is increasing or decreasing for positive and negative values of u. Hence draw arrows on the three curves to indicate the direction of increasing time t.

(v) By referring to your solution curves, explain why this particle will always be removed from the flow by the filter, even if the particle initially moves *away* from the filter.

[**MEI**]

15 The differential equation

$$\frac{dy}{dx} = \frac{y^2 - 4}{(1 + x^{\frac{3}{4}})y}$$

is to be investigated using the tangent field.

(i) State the values of y for which the tangents (direction indicators) are

   (a) parallel to the x axis

   (b) parallel to the y axis.

(ii) Show that the x axis is a line of symmetry for the tangent field.

(iii) Draw up a table of gradients for $x = 0, 0.5, 1.0, 1.5, 2.0$ and $y = 0.5, 1.0$ and 1.5, giving all answers correct to 1 decimal place. Sketch the tangent field for the differential equation for $0 \leqslant x \leqslant 2$, $-2 \leqslant y \leqslant 2$.

(iv) Sketch the solution curve starting at the point $(0, -1)$ and the solution curve starting at the point $(0, -1.5)$.

(v) What does the tangent field suggest about the equation of the solution curve starting from $(0, -2)$? Verify that this equation is the particular solution for this initial condition.

(vi) A particular solution curve starts from the point $(0, k)$, where $0 < |k| < 2$, and x is increasing initially. Describe briefly the behaviour of the solution curve, stating the co-ordinates of the point at which it stops. Why does the solution curve stop at this point?

[MEI]

INVESTIGATION

(i) Display the tangent field for

$$\frac{dy}{dx} = -\frac{(a + x)}{(\beta + y)}$$

using a variety of values for a and β.

Describe the solution curves for the differential equation in terms of a and β. What is the equation of the curves produced?

(ii) Now investigate the solution curves of

$$\frac{dy}{dx} = \frac{(a + x)}{(\beta + y)}.$$

Describe these curves as fully as possible.

KEY POINTS

1 The tangent field is a diagram showing the direction indicators at a number of points.

2 Drawing a tangent field allows you to see the main features of the solution of a differential equation even when you cannot find the solution analytically.

3 An isocline is the locus of points at which the direction indicators have equal gradients.

4 Isoclines are helpful when you are drawing or interpreting tangent fields.

3

Separation of variables

Here and elsewhere we shall not obtain the best insight into things until we actually see them growing from the beginning.

Aristotle

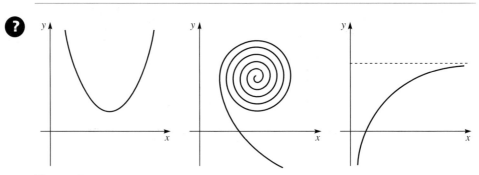

Figure 3.1

Look at the three curves drawn above. For each one, state whether it could be a particular solution of the differential equation

$$\frac{dy}{dx} = kx^n$$

where k is a constant, n a real number (positive or negative, integer or non-integer).

In Chapters 1 and 2 you have seen that differential equations arise in many mathematical problems, and you have met one approximate method of solving first order differential equations. In this chapter you meet a method of finding analytical solutions of some first order differential equations.

There is one class of differential equations that you can already solve analytically. Look at the equation

$$\frac{dy}{dx} = 2x^2.$$

Direct integration gives

c is a constant of integration.

$$y = \int 2x^2 \, dx = \tfrac{2}{3}x^3 + c.$$

You could use direct integration because the differential equation was of the form

$$\frac{dy}{dx} = f(x)$$

and you could integrate the function $f(x)$.

Now look at the differential equation

$$\frac{dy}{dx} = xy^2.$$

This equation cannot be solved by direct integration because the right-hand side contains y as well as x. However, this particular equation is still relatively easy to solve since the right-hand side is a product of a function of x and a function of y. You can proceed as follows.

First you *separate the variables*:

$$\frac{1}{y^2}\frac{dy}{dx} = x$$

> Notice that the right-hand side is now a function of x only, and the left-hand side is $\frac{dy}{dx}$ times a function of y only.

This can be written as

$$\int \frac{1}{y^2}\, dy = \int x\, dx.$$

Now both sides can be integrated separately.

Integrating the left-hand side with respect to y gives

$$\int \frac{1}{y^2}\, dy = -\frac{1}{y} + c_1.$$

Integrating the right-hand side with respect to x gives

$$\int x\, dx = \frac{1}{2}x^2 + c_2.$$

You now have the equation

$$-\frac{1}{y} + c_1 = \frac{1}{2}x^2 + c_2$$

or

$$-\frac{1}{y} = \frac{1}{2}x^2 + c_2 - c_1.$$

This equation includes two arbitrary constants, c_1 and c_2. But since $c_2 - c_1$ is itself an arbitrary constant you would normally replace it with just one constant of integration, c, on the right-hand side:

$$-\frac{1}{y} = \frac{1}{2}x^2 + c$$

or

$$y = -\frac{1}{\frac{1}{2}x^2 + c}.$$

This can be written more tidily as

$$y = -\frac{2}{x^2 + k}$$

where the new arbitrary constant $k = 2c$.

The differential equation $\frac{dy}{dx} = xy^2$ is said to be *separable* because it has the form

$$\frac{dy}{dx} = f(x)\, g(y).$$

> In the case above
> $f(x) = x$
> $g(y) = y^2$

Such an equation can be rewritten in the form

$$\int \frac{1}{g(y)} \, dy = \int f(x) \, dx.$$

EXAMPLE 3.1

Solve the differential equation $\dfrac{dy}{dx} = \dfrac{\sin x}{y^2}$

SOLUTION

Multiplying both sides of the equation by y^2:

$$y^2 \frac{dy}{dx} = \sin x$$

This can be written as

$$\int y^2 \, dy = \int \sin x \, dx$$

$$\tfrac{1}{3} y^3 = -\cos x + c$$

> This process has separated the variables.

$$y = \sqrt[3]{-3\cos x + 3c} = \sqrt[3]{A - 3\cos x}$$

where $A = 3c$ is a constant. This is the general solution of the differential equation.

The same approach is used to solve equations of the form

$$\frac{dy}{dx} = g(y),$$

as in the following examples.

EXAMPLE 3.2

The population, P (in millions), of a country grows so that $\dfrac{dP}{dt} = \dfrac{P}{50}$.

(i) Find the general solution of this differential equation.
(ii) Find the particular solution if $P = 100$ when $t = 0$.

SOLUTION

(i) Dividing both sides of the equation by P gives

$$\frac{1}{P} \frac{dP}{dt} = \frac{1}{50}$$

$$\Rightarrow \quad \int \frac{1}{P} \, dP = \int \frac{1}{50} \, dt$$

$$\ln |P| = \frac{t}{50} + c.$$

Since the population P is always positive, $|P| = P$. Rearranging gives

$$P = e^{\left(\frac{t}{50} + c\right)}$$

which can be written as $P = Ae^{\frac{t}{50}}$ where $A = e^c$.

So the general solution is $P = Ae^{\frac{t}{50}}$.

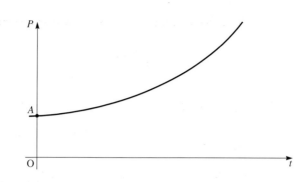

Figure 3.2

Notice that when $t = 0$, $P = A$. This is the initial population, often denoted by P_0.

(ii) To find the particular solution you substitute $P = 100$ and $t = 0$ into the general solution, to obtain

$$100 = Ae^0$$
$$\Rightarrow \quad A = 100.$$

Using this value of A gives the particular solution $P = 100e^{\frac{t}{50}}$.

In the previous example, it was possible to drop the modulus sign because population is always positive: $|P| = P$. It is often not possible to drop the modulus sign, as in the next example.

EXAMPLE 3.3

A drink is placed in a room where the ambient temperature is 20°C. A model for the subsequent temperature, T, of the drink at time t, in hours, is given by Newton's law of cooling. This leads to the differential equation

$$\frac{dT}{dt} = -5\,(T - 20).$$

Find the solution of this differential equation, in the cases where

(i) $T = 80$ when $t = 0$
(ii) $T = 0$ when $t = 0$.

SOLUTION

Dividing both sides of the differential equation by $(T - 20)$, and rewriting it as two integrals:

$$\int \frac{1}{T - 20}\,dT = \int -5\,dt$$
$$\ln|T - 20| = -5t + c$$
$$|T - 20| = e^{(-5t + c)}$$
$$|T - 20| = Ae^{-5t} \quad \text{where } A = e^c.$$

This is the process of separating the variables.

This is the general solution of the differential equation. There are two different initial conditions to consider, and each of these will give a different particular solution.

(i) Here $T > 20$, so $(T - 20)$ is positive and $|T - 20| = T - 20$.

The general solution can therefore be written as

$$T - 20 = Ae^{-5t}$$

or $\qquad T = 20 + Ae^{-5t}.$

Substituting $T = 80$ and $t = 0$ gives

$$80 = 20 + Ae^0 = 20 + A$$
$$\Rightarrow \quad A = 60.$$

The particular solution in this case is $T = 20 + 60e^{-5t}.$

The drink is cooling down to the ambient temperature of 20°C.

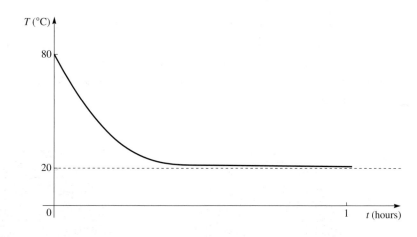

Figure 3.3

(ii) Here $T < 20$, so $(T - 20)$ is negative and $|T - 20| = 20 - T.$

The general solution can therefore be written as

$$20 - T = Ae^{-5t}$$

or $\qquad T = 20 - Ae^{-5t}.$

Substituting $T = 0$ and $t = 0$ gives

$$0 = 20 - Ae^0 = 20 - A$$
$$\Rightarrow \quad A = 20.$$

The particular solution is $T = 20 - 20e^{-5t}.$

The drink is warming up to the ambient temperature of 20°C.

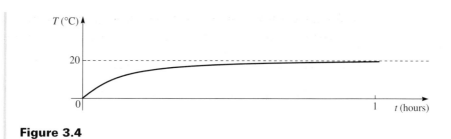

Figure 3.4

Historical note

The discovery of calculus is usually attributed to Isaac Newton with the invention of the *method of fluxions* in 1665, when he was 23 years old, although it is also claimed that Gottfried Leibniz discovered it first but did not publicise his work. The study of differential equations followed on naturally. Newton is known to have solved a differential equation in 1676 but he only published details of it in 1693, the same year in which a differential equation featured in Leibniz's work.

The *method of separation of variables* was developed by Johann Bernoulli between 1694 and 1697. He was a famous teacher and wrote the first calculus textbook in 1696; one of his students was Leonhard Euler (see Chapter 5). Johann Bernoulli was one of the older members of a quite remarkable family of Swiss mathematicians (three of them called Johann) spread over three generations, at least eight of whom may be regarded as famous.

Johann Bernoulli

Gottfried Leibniz

1 Which of the following differential equations can be solved by the method of separation of variables? Give the general solutions of those which can be solved by this method.

(i) $\dfrac{dy}{dx} = y$

(ii) $\dfrac{dy}{dx} = xy$

(iii) $\dfrac{dy}{dx} = x^3 y$

(iv) $\dfrac{dy}{dx} = 3x^2 e^{-y}$

(v) $\dfrac{dy}{dx} = x + yx$

(vi) $\dfrac{dy}{dx} = x + y^2$

(vii) $\dfrac{dy}{dx} = e^{x+y}$

(viii) $\dfrac{dy}{dx} = \dfrac{y}{x(x-1)}$

(ix) $\dfrac{dy}{dx} = x^2 - y^2$

(x) $\dfrac{dy}{dx} = \dfrac{\sin x}{y^2}$

(xi) $\dfrac{dy}{dx} = \dfrac{y+2}{x-2}$

(xii) $\dfrac{dx}{dt} = x^2 - 8x$

2 Find the particular solution of each of the differential equations below for the given conditions.

(i) $x\dfrac{dy}{dx} = y^2$; $y = 10$ when $x = 1$.

(ii) $\dfrac{dy}{dx} = \dfrac{y^2}{x}$; $y = 2$ when $x = 1$.

(iii) $\dfrac{dy}{dx} = \dfrac{x^2}{y}$; $y = 10$ when $x = 1$.

(iv) $\dfrac{dy}{dx} = e^{-y}\sin 2x$; $y = 0$ when $x = 0$.

(v) $\dfrac{dy}{dx} = x^2 e^{-y}$; $y = 10$ when $x = 0$.

(vi) $\dfrac{dy}{dx} = \dfrac{e^y}{y}$; $y = 2$ when $x = 0$.

3 The rate of radioactive decay of a chemical is given by

$$\dfrac{dm}{dt} = -5m.$$

(i) Find the general solution of this equation.

(ii) Given that $m = 10$ when $t = 0$, find the particular solution.

4 A bacterium reproduces such that the rate of increase of the population is given by

$$\dfrac{dP}{dt} = 0.7P, \text{ where } t \text{ is measured in minutes.}$$

(i) Find the general solution of this differential equation.

(ii) Find the particular solution if $P = 100$ when $t = 0$.

(iii) How long does it take for the population to double?

5 An object is projected horizontally on a surface with an initial speed of 20 ms^{-1}. Its speed is modelled by the differential equation

$$\dfrac{dv}{dt} = -\dfrac{v^2}{10}.$$

(i) Find the particular solution of this differential equation that corresponds to the initial condition given.

(ii) How long does it take for the speed to drop to 10% of its original value?

6 Water evaporates from a conical tank such that the rate of change of the height of water is modelled by the differential equation

$$\dfrac{dh}{dt} = -\dfrac{\pi h^2}{4}.$$

(i) Find the general solution of this differential equation.

(ii) Initially the height of the water is H. Find, in terms of H, how long it takes for the height of the water in the tank to decrease by 10%.

7 Water is leaving a tank through a pipe at the bottom, such that the change in the height of water is modelled by the differential equation

$$4\dfrac{dh}{dt} = -\sqrt{20h},$$

where t is in minutes and h in centimetres.

(i) Find the particular solution of this differential equation given that the initial height is 4 cm.

(ii) How long does the tank take to empty?

8 The differential equation below models the motion of a body falling vertically subject to air resistance.

$$\frac{\mathrm{d}v}{\mathrm{d}t} = 10 - 0.2v$$

where v is the downward vertical speed of the body in ms^{-1} and time, t, is measured in seconds.

(i) Find the general solution of the differential equation.

(ii) Find particular solutions when
- **(a)** the body starts from rest
- **(b)** the body has initial downward vertical speed 80 ms^{-1}.

In each case state the terminal velocity.

9 The temperature of a hot body is initially 100°C. It is placed in a tank of water at a temperature of 20°C. The rate of change of temperature is modelled by the differential equation $\frac{\mathrm{d}T}{\mathrm{d}t} = -0.5(T - 20)$, where t is the time in minutes.

(i) Find the particular solution of this differential equation that fits the initial condition given.

(ii) After what time interval has the temperature of the body fallen to 50°C?

10 A small particle moving in a fluid satisfies the differential equation

$$\frac{\mathrm{d}v}{\mathrm{d}t} = -0.2(v + v^2).$$

Find the particular solution of this differential equation given that $v = 40$ when $t = 0$.

11 For the electrical circuit shown below, the current, i amperes, flowing once the switch is closed is given by

L is the inductance measured in henries.

R is the resistance measured in ohms.

$$L\frac{\mathrm{d}i}{\mathrm{d}t} + Ri = V.$$

V is the applied voltage in volts.

(i) If $L = 0.04$, $V = 20$ and $R = 100$, find the general solution of the differential equation.

(ii) If $i = 0$ when $t = 0$ find the particular solution.

(iii) Find the general solution of the original differential equation in terms of R, V and L.

12 A canal lock is modelled as a tank with a rectangular base of area 50 m^2. When the lock is being filled, the height of the water surface above its lowest level is h m at time t, where t is the number of seconds after the lock starts to fill.

In the model, h satisfies the differential equation

$$\frac{\mathrm{d}h}{\mathrm{d}t} = k(2.5 - h), \text{ where } k \text{ is constant.}$$

When $t = 0$, water flows into the lock at a rate of 2 $\mathrm{m}^3\,\mathrm{s}^{-1}$.

(i) Show that initially $\frac{\mathrm{d}h}{\mathrm{d}t} = 0.04$ ms^{-1} and hence that $k = 0.016$.

(ii) Solve the original differential equation for t in terms of h.

The lock is full when $h = 2.5$.

(iii) According to your solution, how long does it take to fill the lock?

(iv) How long would it take for the water level to rise to within 2 mm of the lock being full? (In practice, the lock gates can be opened before the lock is completely full.)

[MEI]

13 A car of mass 1000 kg is initially at rest, and is pushed by a man with a force F newtons. The value of F decreases linearly with respect to the speed $v\,\mathrm{ms}^{-1}$ of the car, as shown in the graph below. The man cannot push when running at a speed greater than $4\,\mathrm{ms^{-1}}$.

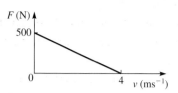

The car is on level ground, and resistances to motion may be neglected.

(i) Show that the motion of the car satisfies the differential equation

$$\frac{\mathrm{d}v}{\mathrm{d}t} = \frac{(4-v)}{8},$$

where t is the time in seconds for which the man has been pushing.

Write down the initial condition.

(ii) Solve the differential equation to show that

$$v = 4(1 - e^{-\frac{t}{8}}).$$

(iii) Sketch the speed–time graph of the car's motion.

(iv) How long does it take the car to reach a speed of $3\,\mathrm{ms^{-1}}$?

[MEI]

14 At 3.00 am one morning the police were called to a house where the body of a murder victim had been found. The police doctor arrived at 3.45 am and took the temperature of the body, which was 34.5°C. One hour later he took the temperature again and measured it to be 33.9°C. The temperature of the room was fairly constant at 15.5°C.

Using Newton's law of cooling as a model, estimate the time of death of the victim. (The normal body temperature of a human being is 37.0°C.)

15 A tank contains 2000 litres of salt solution with an initial concentration of $0.3\ \mathrm{kg\,l^{-1}}$. It is necessary to reduce the concentration to $0.2\ \mathrm{kg\,l^{-1}}$. In order to do this, pure water is pumped into the tank at a rate of 8 litres per minute and the solution is pumped out of the tank at the same rate. The liquid in the tank is stirred so that perfect mixing may be assumed. At time t minutes the mass of salt in the tank is denoted by $M\,\mathrm{kg}$ and the concentration of salt in the solution by $C\,\mathrm{kg\,l^{-1}}$.

(i) Explain how this information leads to the results $\dfrac{\mathrm{d}M}{\mathrm{d}t} = -8C$ and $M = 2000C$.

(ii) Hence form a differential equation for C.

(iii) After how long is the concentration reduced to $0.2\ \mathrm{kg\,l^{-1}}$? Give your answer to the nearest minute.

16 A particle of mass m, travelling through air, experiences a resistive force proportional to its speed v. The resistance is such that in free fall it would reach a terminal speed V.

(i) Determine the value of the constant of proportionality.

The particle is now projected vertically upwards with a speed U.

(ii) Show that at time t after projection its speed v satisfies the differential equation

$$\frac{\mathrm{d}v}{\mathrm{d}t} = -\left(1 + \frac{v}{V}\right)g.$$

(iii) Using $\dfrac{\mathrm{d}v}{\mathrm{d}t} = v\dfrac{\mathrm{d}v}{\mathrm{d}x}$, where x is the height above the point of projection, show that the particle reaches a maximum height of H where

$$H = \frac{V^2}{g}\left\{\frac{U}{V} - \ln\left(1 + \frac{U}{V}\right)\right\}.$$

(iv) Show that if U is much smaller than V then

$$H \approx \frac{U^2}{2g}\left(1 - \frac{2U}{3V}\right).$$

Comment on the significance of this result in terms of the situation being modelled.

[MEI]

17 A car of mass 800 kg travels along a straight horizontal road at $10\,\mathrm{m\,s}^{-1}$. As it passes a point O, the car accelerates by increasing the power from the engine to 40 kW so that the driving force is $\dfrac{40\,000}{v}$ newtons, where $v\,\mathrm{m\,s}^{-1}$ is the speed of the car. The only other horizontal force on the car is a resistance to motion of magnitude $16v$ newtons. The time elapsed after passing O is t seconds and the displacement from O is x metres.

(i) Show that the motion of the car may be modelled by the differential equation

$$50v\frac{\mathrm{d}v}{\mathrm{d}t} = 2500 - v^2,$$

and state the initial conditions.

(ii) Solve the equation to find the particular solution for v in terms of t. Sketch a graph of the solution.

(iii) Formulate a differential equation relating v and x. Solve your equation to show that

$$x = 1250\ln\frac{50+v}{50-v} - 50v + A,$$

where A is a constant. $\left(\text{You are given that}\right.$
$$\frac{v^2}{2500-v^2} = \frac{25}{50+v} + \frac{25}{50-v} - 1\Bigg)$$

(iv) Calculate the displacement after 10 seconds, giving your answer correct to the nearest metre. **[MEI]**

18 A parachutist of mass 80 kg falls vertically from rest from a stationary helicopter. At a distance x m below the helicopter her velocity is $v\,\mathrm{m\,s}^{-1}$. The forces acting on her are her weight and air resistance of magnitude $kv^2\,\mathrm{N}$, where k is a constant. Her terminal velocity is $70\,\mathrm{m\,s}^{-1}$

(i) Show that the motion may be modelled by the differential equation

$$v\frac{\mathrm{d}v}{\mathrm{d}x} = 9.8 - 0.002v^2.$$

(ii) Solve this differential equation to show that $v = 70(1 - \mathrm{e}^{-0.004x})^{\frac{1}{2}}$.

When the parachutist's velocity reaches 99% of its terminal value, she has fallen a distance h m.

(iii) Calculate h.

She then opens her parachute. The magnitude of the resistance force now changes instantly to $80v\,\mathrm{N}$.

(iv) Find her velocity in terms of t, the time in seconds since the parachute opened. Sketch a graph of v against t.

(v) Calculate t when her velocity is $10\,\mathrm{m\,s}^{-1}$. Calculate how far she falls in this time.

[MEI]

19 A rocket of constant mass m is launched vertically from rest on the earth's surface. The forces on the rocket are a thrust from its engines and the force of gravity. The thrust has magnitude Am, where A is a constant. The magnitude of the force due to gravity on the rocket when it is a distance x above the surface of the earth is $\dfrac{R^2mg}{(R+x)^2}$, where R is the radius of the earth and g is the acceleration due to gravity at the earth's surface.

The rocket has velocity v at a distance x above the earth's surface.

(i) Write down a differential equation connecting v and x. Solve the equation to show that

$$v^2 = 2Ax - \frac{2Rgx}{R+x}.$$

The thrust on the rocket ceases when $x = a$. Subsequently, the only force acting is due to gravity.

(ii) Solve an appropriate differential equation to show that, for the motion after the thrust ceases,

$$v^2 = \frac{2R^2g}{R+x} + 2(Aa - Rg).$$

(iii) Determine the range of values of a for which the rocket will fall back to earth.

(iv) If the rocket does not fall back to earth, find its terminal velocity.

[MEI]

20 This problem concerns the growth of sweet peas in John Berry's garden in Devon last summer. Two dozen plants were grown and their average heights were recorded every seven days. The average height when measurements began was 8 cm.

week	height (cm)
0	8
1	14
2	26
3	47
4	69
5	93
6	121
7	146
8	162
9	177
10	182

(i) An initial model assumes that the rate of growth of a plant is proportional to its height h. Formulate a differential equation for this model.

(ii) Solve the differential equation, using the initial condition and the average height after week 1 to find the two unknown constants in the solution. This is called the *exponential model.*

(iii) Plot the real data, and superimpose a graph of the exponential model. Criticise the exponential model. Give reasons why you think it does not fit the data for higher values of t.

(iv) A revised model is the *logistic differential equation*

$$\frac{dh}{dt} = ah\left(1 - \frac{h}{H}\right),$$

where H is the final ('equilibrium') height of the sweet pea plants and a is a constant. Without solving this equation, explain why it might be an improvement on the exponential model.

(v) Solve the logistic differential equation. Use the data in the table for weeks 0, 5 and 10 to find the unknown constants in the solution.

(vi) Calculate the table of values for the logistic model for $t = 0$ to $t = 10$. Comment on the appropriateness of the logistic equation as a model.

21 A simple model of the progression of a virus is being formulated. A closed population of constant size 10^5 consists entirely of those infected by the virus (*infectives*) and those not yet infected (*susceptibles*). The rate of increase of infectives is proportional to the product of the number I of these infectives and the number S of susceptibles where $I + S = 10^5$. Time t is measured in weeks.

(i) Show that

$$\frac{dI}{dt} = kI(10^5 - I)$$

where k is a constant of proportionality and write down an equivalent equation for $\frac{dS}{dt}$ in terms of S.

Initially 1% of the population are infectives and it is noted that 10 weeks later this has risen to 20%.

(ii) Show that to 3 significant figures $k = 3.21 \times 10^{-6}$.

(iii) Find I as a function of time and hence find S as a function of time.

(iv) Verify that your expression for S in part (iii) satisfies the differential equation in part (i) and the initial conditions.

(v) Determine the time at which the number of infectives equals the number of susceptibles.

[MEI]

22 The pressure P, density ρ and absolute temperature T in the atmosphere at a height z above the Earth's surface are related by the equations

$$P = R\rho T, \qquad \frac{\mathrm{d}T}{\mathrm{d}z} = -a, \qquad \frac{\mathrm{d}P}{\mathrm{d}z} = -\rho g.$$

In these equations, a and R are constants and g is the acceleration due to gravity.

Also, at $z = 0$, $T = T_0$, $P = P_0$ and $\rho = \rho_0$.

(i) Show that $T = T_0 - az$. Hence show that

$$\frac{\mathrm{d}P}{\mathrm{d}z} = \frac{-gP}{R(T_0 - az)}.$$

In the 'standard atmosphere' used in aeronautics, the values of the constants in SI units are $T_0 = 300$, $a = 0.0065$, $R = 8.3$ and $g = 9.8$.

(ii) Show that the pressure P at a height z is given approximately by

$$P = P_0 \left(1 - \frac{z}{46\,000}\right)^{180}.$$

In a 'barotropic' fluid, the density is a function only of pressure. In the atmosphere, this gives the relation $\dfrac{\rho}{\rho_0} = \left(\dfrac{P}{P_0}\right)^m$ where m is a positive constant, and $0 < m < 1$.

(iii) Explain why $P_0 = R\rho_0 T_0$ and

$$P^{-m}\frac{\mathrm{d}P}{\mathrm{d}z} = \frac{-\rho_0 g}{P_0^{\,m}}.$$

Hence prove that

$$P = P_0 \left(1 - \frac{g(1-m)}{RT_0}z\right)^{\frac{1}{1-m}}.$$

(iv) Can the constant m be chosen to make the expressions for P in parts (ii) and (iii) consistent? Explain your answer.

23 Water is draining from an open-topped container through a small hole as shown in the diagram. The surface of the water is x cm above the hole, and the speed of the water as it emerges from the hole is $v\,\mathrm{cm\,s^{-1}}$.

(i) If the horizontal cross-section of the container has area $A\,\mathrm{cm^2}$ and the hole has area $B\,\mathrm{cm^2}$, explain briefly why

$$A\frac{\mathrm{d}x}{\mathrm{d}t} = -Bv, \qquad \qquad ①$$

where t is the time in seconds.

Torricelli's law states that, in this case,

$$v^2 = 1960x. \qquad \qquad ②$$

(ii) In the case where $A = 400$ and $B = 2$, use equations ① and ② to eliminate v. Find the solution for x in terms of t, given that initially the water surface is 25 cm above the hole.

A new container is used which has a variable cross-sectional area given by $A = 300 + 30x$. It has a small hole of area $2\,\mathrm{cm^2}$ near its base. Initially the water surface is 25 cm above the hole. Equations ① and ② still apply.

(iii) Formulate and solve a differential equation to find the time it takes for the water level to reach the hole.

A container is to be designed with a variable cross-sectional area such that the depth of water decreases at a constant rate.

(iv) Given that the cross-sectional area is $1000\,\mathrm{cm^2}$ when $x = 25$, find an expression for the cross-sectional area in terms of x.

[MEI]

24 Take $g = 10\,\text{ms}^{-2}$ throughout this question. In working out a new routine, a team of sky divers decide they need $1000\,\text{m}$ of freefall in order to complete their complex patterns. The resistance to motion is taken to be proportional to the speed v. The leader of the team has a total mass, including equipment, of $80\,\text{kg}$ and a terminal (i.e. limiting) speed of $40\,\text{ms}^{-1}$.

(i) If $t\,\text{s}$ is the time taken to fall a distance $x\,\text{m}$, show that the speed $v\,\text{ms}^{-1}$ of the leader is given by the equation

$$4\frac{dv}{dt} = 40 - v,$$

and write down appropriate initial conditions for x and v.

(ii) By solving this equation, find a relation between v and t. Hence show that

$$x = 40t - 160(1 - e^{-\frac{t}{4}}).$$

(iii) Write down the time $T\,\text{s}$ which would be taken by the leader in falling $1000\,\text{m}$ at terminal speed.

(iv) Find the actual distance $D\,\text{m}$ fallen by the leader in $T\,\text{s}$.

(v) Find the time it takes the leader to reach a speed of $39.9\,\text{ms}^{-1}$. Is this achieved in the freefall period?

[**MEI**]

25 A battery is being charged. The charging rate is modelled by $\frac{dq}{dt} = k(Q - q)$, where q is the charge in the battery (measured in ampere-hours) at time t (measured in hours). Q is the maximum charge the battery can store and k is a constant of proportionality. The model is valid for $q \geqslant 0.4Q$.

It is given that $q = \lambda Q$ when $t = 0$, where λ is a constant such that $0.4 \leqslant \lambda < 1$.

(i) Solve the differential equation to find q in terms of t. Sketch the graph of the solution.

It is noticed that the charging rate halves every 40 minutes.

(ii) Show that $k = \frac{3}{2}\ln 2$.

Charging is always stopped when $q = 0.95Q$.

(iii) If T is the time until charging is stopped, show that $T = \dfrac{2\ln[20(1 - \lambda)]}{3\ln 2}$ for $0.4 \leqslant \lambda \leqslant 0.95$.

(iv) On successive days, the battery was charged. On the first day the initial charge was $0.4Q$. On the second day the initial charge was $0.7Q$. Calculate the difference in the time taken to charge the battery on the two days. How could this have been predicted from the information given in the question without solving the differential equation?

[**MEI**]

26 A ball of mass $0.1\,\text{kg}$ is projected vertically upwards from ground level with an initial speed of $49\,\text{m s}^{-1}$. When the ball is in flight, the forces acting on it are its weight and air resistance which is assumed to have magnitude $0.02v$ newtons, where $v\,\text{m s}^{-1}$ is the velocity of the ball. The time after projection is denoted by t seconds.

(i) Show that, for the upward motion, $\dfrac{dv}{dt} = -0.2(49 + v)$. Hence find an expression for v in terms of t.

The ball reaches a maximum height of H metres when $t = T_1$.

(ii) Calculate T_1 and show that $H = 245\,(1 - \ln 2)$.

(iii) Explain briefly why the differential equation in part (i) and its solution apply unchanged to the downward motion as well as the upward motion.

The ball reaches the ground again when $t = T_2$.

(iv) Show that $\frac{1}{10}T_2 + e^{-0.2T_2} = 1$.

[**MEI**]

COFFEE COOLING

Newton's law of cooling says that, in well-ventilated conditions, the rate of cooling of an object is proportional to the temperature difference between the object and its surroundings. Investigate whether this is an appropriate model for a cup of hot coffee in a room with the door and windows closed. If not, use your data to suggest a better model.

FISH STOCKS

The fish in oceans, rivers and lakes constitute a major food source. However with the introduction of modern fishing methods there is the danger of some species being overfished to the point where their numbers are seriously reduced; in extreme cases there is risk of extinction.

In this investigation you are to consider the effect of fishing on a single species at time t in a limited environment. The population of the species at time t is P, and the maximum the environment can sustain is P_m.

The rate of change of the population is given by

$$\frac{dP}{dt} = I - D.$$

The variable D is the rate of decrease caused by fishing, and it depends upon the fishing strategy. The variable I is the rate of natural increase, given by

$I = kP(P_m - P)$ where k is a constant.

This is called the logistic model.

Investigate the following two cases.

(i) Constant catch: in this case $D = c$, a constant.

(ii) Periodic harvesting: in this case $D = 0$, but at regular intervals P is reduced by a fixed amount.

KEY POINTS

1 The method of separation of variables can be used to solve first order differential equations of the form

$$\frac{dy}{dx} = f(x)g(y).$$

2 Separating the variables gives

$$\int \frac{1}{g(y)} dy = \int f(x) dx.$$

Integrating factors

4

There is no branch of mathematics, however abstract, which may not some day be applied to phenomena of the real world.

Nikolai Lobatchevsky

? Which of the following differential equations can be written in the form $\dfrac{dy}{dx} = f(x)g(y)$ and which cannot?

(i) $\dfrac{dy}{dx} = x^2 + x^2 y$ **(ii)** $\dfrac{dy}{dx} = x^2 - xy$

(iii) $\dfrac{dy}{dx} = x^2 + x + xy + y$ **(iv)** $\dfrac{dy}{dx} = x + y^2$

When a first order differential equation cannot be written in the form $\dfrac{dy}{dx} = f(x)g(y)$, it cannot be solved using the method of separation of variables.

If however it is a *linear* equation, you can multiply it by a special function called an *integrating factor* which converts it to a form which can be integrated. This method is the subject of this chapter.

Linear equations

A linear differential equation is one in which the independent variable (y in these examples) only appears to the power of 1. So the differential equation $\dfrac{dy}{dx} = x^2 - xy$ is linear because the only terms that involve y are $\dfrac{dy}{dx}$ and $-xy$.

There are no terms in y^2, $\sqrt{y}$, $\sin y$, $\left(\dfrac{dy}{dx}\right)^2$, etc. (Strictly it is linear in y.)

Any linear first order differential equation may be written in the form

$$\frac{dy}{dx} + Py = Q$$

where P and Q are functions of x only.

For example, the equation $\dfrac{dy}{dx} = x^2 - xy$

can be rewritten as $\dfrac{dy}{dx} + xy = x^2.$

This is in the form $\dfrac{dy}{dx} + Py = Q,$

where the functions P and Q are given by $P = x$ and $Q = x^2$.

 Which of the four equations given at the start of the chapter are linear?
Identify the functions P and Q for each of those equations.

Look at the next two examples. They concern linear differential equations that
can be solved by close inspection.

EXAMPLE 4.1

Find the general solution of the differential equation

$$(\cos x)\dfrac{dy}{dx} - (\sin x)y = x^2.$$

SOLUTION

The equation looks forbidding until you notice that the left-hand side is a
perfect derivative.

Since $\dfrac{d}{dx}(\cos x) = -\sin x$, it follows (using the product rule) that

$$\dfrac{d}{dx}(y\cos x) = \dfrac{dy}{dx}\cos x - y\sin x.$$

> This is the left-hand side
> of the differential equation.

So you can rewrite the differential equation as

$$\dfrac{d}{dx}(y\cos x) = x^2.$$

You may now integrate both sides to obtain

$$y\cos x = \int x^2\, dx = \dfrac{x^3}{3} + c.$$

Dividing both sides by $\cos x$, the general solution is

$$y = \dfrac{x^3}{3\cos x} + \dfrac{c}{\cos x}.$$

In example 4.1 the left-hand side was already a perfect derivative. That is not the
case in the next example but it is a simple matter to convert it into one.

EXAMPLE 4.2

Find the general solution of the differential equation

$$\frac{dy}{dx} + \frac{2}{x}y = \frac{4}{x^2} \quad \text{for } x \neq 0.$$

SOLUTION

First note that the equation is linear, because it can be written in the form

$$\frac{dy}{dx} + Py = Q$$

where $P = \frac{2}{x}$ and $Q = \frac{4}{x^2}$. There are no terms in y^2, $\frac{1}{y}$, $\sqrt{y}$, etc.

If you now multiply through by x^2, the equation becomes

$$x^2 \frac{dy}{dx} + 2xy = 4.$$

The left-hand side of this equation is now the expression you obtain when you differentiate x^2y with respect to x, using the product rule:

$$\frac{d}{dx}(x^2y) = x^2 \frac{dy}{dx} + 2xy.$$

So the differential equation can be rewritten as

$$\frac{d}{dx}(x^2y) = 4.$$

Now integrating both sides gives

$$x^2y = \int 4 \, dx = 4x + c.$$

The general solution is

$$y = \frac{4}{x} + \frac{c}{x^2}.$$

In examples 4.1 and 4.2 the differential equations could be rewritten in the form

$$\frac{d}{dx}(Ry) = \text{function of } x$$

where R was some function of x. In the first example $R = \cos x$, and in the second, $R = x^2$. Once the differential equation was written in this form, it was a straightforward task to solve it, since all that remained was to integrate the function of x on the right-hand side.

However in the second example we had to multiply each term in the equation by a factor x^2 to bring the left-hand side into the required form. This factor of x^2 is an example of an *integrating factor*; multiplying by it made the left-hand side a perfect derivative.

ACTIVITY Write the following differential equations in the form

$$\frac{\mathrm{d}}{\mathrm{d}x}(Ry) = \text{function of } x$$

and then find their general solutions.

(i) $x^3 \dfrac{\mathrm{d}y}{\mathrm{d}x} + 3x^2 y = 2e^x$

(ii) $e^{3x} \dfrac{\mathrm{d}y}{\mathrm{d}x} + 3e^{3x} y = x$

(iii) $\dfrac{\mathrm{d}y}{\mathrm{d}x} - \dfrac{1}{x} y = x^2.$

Part **(iii)** of the activity was harder than the others because the differential equation was written in the standard form

$$\frac{\mathrm{d}y}{\mathrm{d}x} + Py = Q.$$

 Notice that the coefficient of $\frac{\mathrm{d}y}{\mathrm{d}x}$ is 1.

When the equation is in this form, you need to multiply each term by a function R of x, so that it becomes

$$R\frac{\mathrm{d}y}{\mathrm{d}x} + RPy = RQ.$$

Notice that the right-hand side is still a function of x only.

The function R has to be chosen such that the left-hand side can be rewritten as $\dfrac{\mathrm{d}}{\mathrm{d}x}(Ry)$. You must therefore choose R such that

$$\frac{\mathrm{d}}{\mathrm{d}x}(Ry) \equiv R\frac{\mathrm{d}y}{\mathrm{d}x} + RPy.$$

Differentiating the left-hand side, this becomes

$$R\frac{\mathrm{d}y}{\mathrm{d}x} + \frac{\mathrm{d}R}{\mathrm{d}x}y \equiv R\frac{\mathrm{d}y}{\mathrm{d}x} + RPy.$$

This is true if $\dfrac{\mathrm{d}R}{\mathrm{d}x} = RP,$

or $\quad \dfrac{1}{R}\dfrac{\mathrm{d}R}{\mathrm{d}x} = P.$

This can be integrated by separating the variables to give

$$\ln R = \int P \, \mathrm{d}x$$
$$\text{and so} \quad R = e^{\int P \mathrm{d}x}.$$

This means that any first order linear equation written in the standard form $\dfrac{\mathrm{d}y}{\mathrm{d}x} + Py = Q$ can be multiplied by an *integrating factor* $R = e^{\int P \mathrm{d}x}$ to convert it to the compact form: $\dfrac{\mathrm{d}}{\mathrm{d}x}(Ry) = RQ.$

You can then solve the equation by integrating the right-hand side, which is a function of x only.

EXAMPLE 4.3

Solve the differential equation

$$x\frac{dy}{dx} + 2y = \frac{4}{x} \text{ for } x \neq 0.$$

SOLUTION

Dividing through by x gives the equation in standard form:

$$\frac{dy}{dx} + \frac{2}{x}y = \frac{4}{x^2}.$$

> This is the equation that was solved by inspection in example 4.2 but this time it was not presented in standard form.

Comparing this with $\frac{dy}{dx} + Py = Q$ gives $P = \frac{2}{x}$ and $Q = \frac{4}{x^2}$.

The integrating factor is
$$\begin{aligned}
R &= e^{\int P\,dx} \\
&= e^{\int \frac{2}{x}dx} \\
&= e^{2\ln x} \\
&= e^{\ln x^2} \\
&= x^2.
\end{aligned}$$

Multiplying the equation in standard form by this integrating factor gives

$$x^2\frac{dy}{dx} + 2xy = 4.$$

The left-hand side is now the derivative of a product, and can be written as $\frac{d}{dx}(Ry)$. In this case $R = x^2$ so that the left-hand side is $\frac{d}{dx}(x^2y)$.

So the equation can be written

$$\frac{d}{dx}(x^2y) = 4$$
$$\Rightarrow \quad x^2y = 4x + c.$$

Dividing by x^2 gives the general solution

$$y = \frac{4}{x} = \frac{c}{x^2}.$$

This is of course the same solution as the one obtained in example 4.2. Now, however, you have a method for finding an integrating factor, whereas previously you were relying on spotting a convenient form for the left-hand side.

Now check that you can follow the stages in the next two examples.

EXAMPLE 4.4

Find the solution of the differential equation

$$x^2\frac{dy}{dx} + xy = \frac{2}{x}$$

that satisfies the condition $y = 1$ when $x = 2$.

SOLUTION

First the differential equation is written in standard form by dividing each term by x^2:

$$\frac{dy}{dx} + \frac{1}{x}y = \frac{2}{x^3}.$$

In this case $P = \frac{1}{x}$ and $Q = \frac{2}{x^3}$. The integrating factor is

$$R = e^{\int P\,dx}$$
$$= e^{\int \frac{1}{x}dx}$$
$$= e^{\ln x}$$
$$= x.$$

Multiplying the differential equation by the integrating factor gives

$$x\frac{dy}{dx} + y = x \times \frac{2}{x^3}$$

or

$$\frac{d}{dx}(xy) = \frac{2}{x^2}.$$

Integrating with respect to x gives

$$xy = \int \frac{2}{x^2}dx$$
$$= -\frac{2}{x} + c.$$

Dividing by x gives the general solution as

$$y = -\frac{2}{x^2} + \frac{c}{x}.$$

The condition given is $y = 1$ when $x = 2$, and substituting these values in the general solution gives

$$1 = -\frac{2}{4} + \frac{c}{2}$$

and so $c = 3$.

The particular solution of the differential equation is

$$y = -\frac{2}{x^2} + \frac{3}{x}.$$

EXAMPLE 4.5

Use the integrating factor method to find the general solution of the differential equation

$$(\cos x)\frac{dy}{dx} - (\sin x)y = x^2.$$

SOLUTION

The equation is written in standard form by dividing through by $\cos x$:

$$\frac{dy}{dx} - \frac{\sin x}{\cos x}y = \frac{x^2}{\cos x}.$$

Here $P = -\dfrac{\sin x}{\cos x}$ and $Q = \dfrac{x^2}{\cos x}$.

The integrating factor is $R = e^{\left(\int -\frac{\sin x}{\cos x}dx\right)}$

$$= e^{(\ln(\cos x))}$$

$$= \cos x.$$

Multiplying through by $\cos x$ gives

$$\frac{dy}{dx}\cos x - y\sin x = x^2.$$

$$\Rightarrow \quad \frac{dy}{dx}(y\cos x) = x^2.$$

This is integrated to give $y\cos x = \dfrac{x^3}{3} + c.$

Dividing through by $\cos x$ gives the general solution

$$y = \frac{x^3}{3\cos x} + \frac{c}{\cos x}.$$

This is the general solution of the differential equation.

Note

The integrating factor method involves several steps that can introduce errors, so it is important to verify that the function you think is the answer does indeed satisfy the original differential equation.

Historical note

There is some uncertainty as to who discovered integrating factors. Some claim the credit for Leibniz who died in 1716 but the invention is generally believed to have been made somewhat later by Euler in 1734 and, independently, by Fontaine and Clairaut.

Claude Clairaut was a child prodigy who wrote a paper on third order curves at the age of 10 and followed it up shortly afterwards with one on the differential geometry of twisted curves in space. His brother was also a prodigy but died at the age of 16 having already completed original work on geometry.

1 Find the integrating factor for each of the following differential equations.

(i) $\dfrac{dy}{dx} + x^2 y = x$

(ii) $\dfrac{dy}{dx} + y\sin x = x$

(iii) $4x\dfrac{dy}{dx} - y = x^2$

(iv) $x^2\dfrac{dy}{dx} + xy = 2$

(v) $\dfrac{dy}{dx} + 7y = 1$

(vi) $\cos x\dfrac{dy}{dx} + y\sin x = e^{-2x}$

2 Find the particular solution of each of the following differential equations.

(i) $x\dfrac{dy}{dx} + 2y = x^2;$ $y = 0$ when $x = 1.$

(ii) $\dfrac{dy}{dx} + xy = 4x;$ $y = 2$ when $x = 0.$

(iii) $6xy + \dfrac{dy}{dx} = 0;$ $y = 3$ when $x = 1.$

(iv) $\dfrac{dy}{dx} - 2xy = x;$ $y = 1$ when $x = 0.$

(v) $\dfrac{dy}{dx} - \dfrac{3}{x}y = x;$ $y = 0$ when $x = 1.$

(vi) $\dfrac{dy}{dx} + 3x^2 y = x^2;$ $y = -1$ when $x = 0.$

3 An object falling vertically experiences air resistance so that the velocity satisfies the differential equation

$$\dfrac{dv}{dt} = 10 - 0.4v$$

(i) Use the integrating factor method to find the general solution of this differential equation.

(ii) If initially $v = 0$, find the particular solution.

(iii) Solve the equation using the method of separation of variables.

(iv) Compare your two solutions.

(v) If a linear differential equation is separable, which of the two methods would you prefer to use, the intergrating factor method or the method of separation of variables?

4 A parachutist has a terminal speed of 30 ms^{-1}. The magnitude of the air resistance acting when the parachute is open is modelled by $F = kmv$ newtons, where k is a constant, v is the speed and m is the mass of the parachutist.

(i) Find the value for k, taking the acceleration due to gravity to be 10 ms^{-2}.

(ii) Formulate a first order differential equation for the velocity, v.

(iii) Use the integrating factor method to find the general solution of the differential equation.

(iv) Find the particular solution if the parachutist is moving at 60 ms^{-1} when the parachute opens.

5 The radioactive isotope uranium-238 decays into thorium-234 which in turn decays into protactinium-234. This can be summarised as

$$^{238}_{92}U \xrightarrow{k_1} \,^{234}_{90}Th \xrightarrow{k_2} \,^{234}_{91}Pa$$

where k_1 and k_2 are reaction constants $(k_1 \neq k_2)$. The amounts of uranium-238, thorium-234 and protactinium-234 at time t are denoted by x, y and z. An experiment begins with an amount a of uranium-238 present, but no thorium-234 or proactinium-234. The amount y of thorium-234 present at time t satisfies the differential equation

$$\dfrac{dy}{dt} + k_2 y = k_1 a e^{-k_1 t}.$$

(i) Find the integrating factor for the differential equation and hence its general solution.

(ii) Find the particular solution that satisfies the initial conditions.

(iii) Write down differential equations governing x and z. (You may assume that the rate of decay of an isotope is proportional to the amount present).

(iv) The differential equation given in this problem is common in radioactive decay. Investigate what would happen in a case where $k_1 = k_2$.

6 (i) Use the substitution $x = e^u$ to show that

$$\int \frac{1}{x}(\ln x)^n \, dx = \frac{1}{n+1}(\ln x)^{n+1} + C$$

for $n \neq -1$ and find the corresponding result for $n = -1$.

The differential equation

$$y' + \frac{y}{x\ln x} = \frac{1}{x},$$

with $y = 1$ when $x = e$,

is to be solved using an integrating factor.

(ii) Find the integrating factor.

(iii) Solve the differential equation.

(iv) Sketch the solution curve for $x > 1$.

[MEI]

7 The differential equation governing the current I amps in an electric circuit containing a resistor of R ohms, a capacitor of C farads and an applied electromotive force of E volts, all in series, is

$$R\frac{dI}{dt} + \frac{I}{C} = \frac{dE}{dt},$$

where R and C are constants and t is time.

Initially the current is monitored with $E = E_0$, provided by a battery, and subsequently with $E = E_0 \sin \omega t$, provided by a generator.

Find the solution of the differential equation in each of the cases.

(i) $E = E_0$, a constant, and initially $I = I_0$,

(ii) $E = E_0 \sin \omega t$, where both E_0 and ω are constants, and initially $I = 0$.

$$\left[\text{The result, } \int e^{at} \cos bt \, dt \right.$$

$$= \frac{e^{at}}{a^2 + b^2}(a\cos bt + b\sin bt) + c,$$

$$\left. \text{may be assumed.}\right]$$

[MEI]

8 The differential equation

$$\frac{dy}{dx}\sin x - y\cos x = e^{-kx}\sin^2 x \qquad (k \geqslant 0)$$

is to be solved, where k is a constant.

(i) Show that $\frac{d}{dx}(\ln \sin x) = \cot x$.

(ii) In the case $k > 0$, solve the differential equation to show that the general solution is

$$y = \left(A - \frac{1}{k}e^{-kx}\right)\sin x,$$

where A is an arbitrary constant.

(iii) Find the particular solution in the cases

(a) $\dfrac{dy}{dx} = \dfrac{1}{k}$ when $x = 0$

(b) $\dfrac{dy}{dx} = -\dfrac{1}{k}$ when $x = 0$

Describe the differences in the behaviour of the two solutions for large positive values of x.

(iv) In the case $k = 0$, find the general solution of the equation. Describe its behaviour for large positive values of x.

[MEI]

9 The function $y = f(x)$ satisfies the differential equation

$$x\frac{dy}{dx} + 2y = \sqrt{1 + x^2}.$$

(i) Using the integrating factor method, or otherwise, find the general solution of this differential equation.

(ii) Find the particular solution which satisfies the condition that $y = 1$ when $x = 1$. How does y behave when x becomes very small?

(iii) Write down the first three non-zero terms in the expansion of $(1 + x^2)^{\frac{3}{2}}$ in ascending powers of x.

(iv) Using the expansion in part (iii) and the general solution found in part (i), write down the power series expansion of the general solution y for small values of x up to and including the term in x^2. Hence find the particular solution of the differential equation which crosses the y axis from the region $x > 0$ into the region $x < 0$. Is it possible to obtain other solutions of the differential equation in the region $x < 0$? Explain your answer.

[MEI]

10 The differential equation

$$(1-x)\frac{dy}{dx} + \frac{2}{1+x}y = (1-x)^2$$

is to be solved for values of x in the interval $-1 < x < 1$.

(i) Solve the differential equation for y in terms of x.

$$\left(\text{Assume that } \frac{2}{1-x^2} \equiv \frac{1}{1-x} + \frac{1}{1+x} \right)$$

(ii) Find the solutions in the cases
  (a) $y = 0$ when $x = 0$
  (b) $y = 1$ when $x = 0$.
  In each case state the behaviour of the solution as $x \rightarrow -1$.

(iii) Show that there is one solution for which y tends to a finite limit as x tends to -1. State this solution and sketch its graph.

[MEI]

11 A raindrop of mass 5×10^{-6} kg falls vertically from rest. The forces acting on it are its weight and air resistance of magnitude $4 \times 10^{-6}v$N, where $v\,\text{ms}^{-1}$ is the velocity of the raindrop.

(i) Show that the motion may be modelled by

$$5\frac{dv}{dt} = 49 - 4v,$$

and state the initial condition for v.

(ii) Solve the differential equation to find v in terms of t. Sketch a graph of the solution.

An identical raindrop falls vertically from rest through mist. Water condenses on the raindrop as it falls, and you are given that its motion may be modelled by the equation

$$(t+5)\frac{dv}{dt} + 5v = 9.8(t+5).$$

(iii) Solve this equation to find v in terms of t.
(iv) Sketch a graph of the solution.

[MEI]

12 A solution is sought to the differential equation

$$\frac{dy}{dx} + \frac{y}{x} = \sin x \quad (x > 0).$$

(i) Find the general solution for y in terms of x.

(ii) Given that $y = \dfrac{1}{\sqrt{2}}$ when $x = \frac{1}{4}\pi$, find y when $x = \pi$.

[MEI]

13 The solution is sought for the differential equation

$$(1+x^2)\frac{dy}{dx} - \frac{4x^3y}{1-x^2} = 1 \quad (-1 < x < 1).$$

(i) Solve the equation to show that

$$y = \frac{k + 3x - x^3}{3(1-x^4)}, \quad \circledast$$

where k is an arbitrary contrast.

(ii) Find the particular solution in each of the cases
  (a) $y = 1$ when $x = 0$
  (b) $y = 0$ when $x = 0$.

In each case, draw a sketch graph of the solution for $-1 < x < 1$.

(iii) Find the value of k in $\circledast$ for which y tends to a finite limit as x tends to 1.

[MEI]

14 The differential equation

$$\frac{dy}{dx} + \frac{y}{1+x} = x^{\frac{3}{2}} \quad x \geqslant 0$$

is to be solved.

(i) Find the particular solution subject to the initial condition $x = 0$, $y = 2$. Describe the behaviour of the solution as x tends to infinity.

A more general case of the above equation is

$$(1+x)\frac{dy}{dx} + ny = x^{\frac{3}{2}}(1+x)^{2-n} \quad x \geqslant 0,$$

where n is a real number.

(ii) Solve the differential equation to show that the general solution is

$$y = \frac{2x^{\frac{5}{2}}(7 + 5x) + C}{35(1 + x)^n},$$

where C is an arbitrary constant.

(iii) Describe the behaviour of the general solution as x tends to infinity, identifying three distinct cases and the values of n for which they occur.

[MEI]

KEY POINTS

1 Any first order linear differential equation can be written in the form

$$\frac{dy}{dx} + Py = Q$$

where P and Q are functions of x only.

2 To solve the equation $\dfrac{dy}{dx} + Py = Q$ you multiply throughout by the integrating factor $R = e^{\int P \, dx}$. The solution is then given by

$$Ry = \int RQ \, dx.$$

Euler's method

The age of chivalry has gone. That of ... calculators has succeeded and the glory of Europe is extinguished for ever.

E. Burke, 1792

? Figure 5.1 shows a computer-generated tangent field for the differential equation

$$\frac{dy}{dx} = -\frac{x}{y}$$

together with the particular solution curve with initial condition $y = 0$ when $x = -2$.

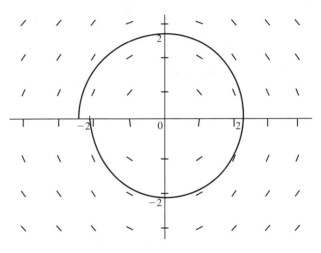

Figure 5.1

(i) Solve the equation analytically and so find the equation of the required particular solution. Describe the curve this equation represents.

(ii) How can you tell that the computer has gone wrong? Why has it happened?

There are many first order differential equations which cannot be solved analytically. Look at the non-linear differential equation

$$\frac{dy}{dx} = x^2 + y^2.$$

You cannot separate the variables in this equation because it is not of the form

$$\frac{dy}{dx} = f(x)g(y).$$

Neither can you use an integrating factor, because the equation is not of the linear form

$$\frac{dy}{dx} + Py = Q.$$

Although there are many more analytical methods for solving first order differential equations than are covered in this book, it is often difficult or even impossible to solve a differential equation by analytical methods. In this case a numerical method of solution must be used.

In this chapter you will meet the simplest numerical method for solving differential equations. It is called *Euler's method.*

Straight line segments

The idea behind Euler's method is to approximate the solution curve (which you cannot find exactly) by a sequence of straight lines. The gradient of each straight line is the same as the gradient of the direction indicator in the tangent field at the start of the line.

As an example, take the differential equation

$$\frac{dy}{dx} = x^2 + y^2$$

with initial condition $y = 1$ when $x = 1$. Since you cannot solve the differential equation analytically, you cannot find an equation for the solution curve through the point $(1, 1)$. Euler's method allows you to find an approximation to the actual curve, using the initial conditions and the information you have about the gradient of the curve.

The slope of the direction indicator at the point $(1, 1)$ is given by

$$\frac{dy}{dx} = 1^2 + 1^2 = 2.$$

Figure 5.2 shows a line segment AB starting at point A $(1, 1)$ with gradient 2. The broken line represents the actual (but unknown) solution curve through $(1, 1)$. You can see that the line segment is a tangent to this solution curve at $(1, 1)$. This line segment is the first part of your approximate curve. To find the next part of the curve you need a new starting point.

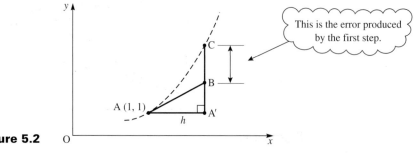

This is the error produced by the first step.

Figure 5.2

After a step size h in the x direction, the exact solution is an unknown point C and the estimate using the straight line segment is at B. The error in using B instead of C is BC.

If $h = 0.2$ then you can see that in triangle AA'B

$$\frac{A'B}{AA'} = \text{gradient of tangent AB} = 2$$

$$A'B = 2AA' = 2h = 0.4.$$

The estimates for the co-ordinates of point B are $x = 1.2$ and $y = 1.4$. The next line segment will start from B (1.2, 1.4) and have the same gradient as the direction indicator at B. It is shown as the line BD in figure 5.3. The gradient of BD is $1.2^2 + 1.4^2 = 3.4$.

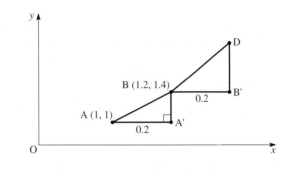

Figure 5.3

The co-ordinates of point D can be obtained from triangle BB'D in figure 5.3, using the fact that the gradient of BD is 3.4:

$$DB' = 0.2 \times 3.4 = 0.68.$$

D is therefore the point (1.4, 2.08).

Figure 5.4 shows such a process over several steps. Usually the further you move away from the starting point the larger is the error between the sequence of line segments and the actual solution curve. The error can usually be reduced by taking smaller steps.

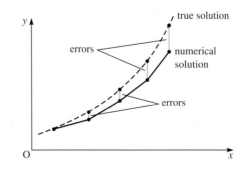

Figure 5.4

You will realise that drawing a sequence of straight lines from a tangent field is a rather painstaking and slow method. The advantage of Euler's method is that you can formulate a simple rule to generate the co-ordinates of points B, C, … numerically as a table of values. This means that the process can easily be programmed into a calculator or computer, or carried out on a spreadsheet.

Suppose you have a tangent field defined by the differential equation

$$\frac{dy}{dx} = f(x, y)$$

and after n steps you have estimated the value of y at x_n to be y_n. With a step length of h, and with (x_0, y_0) as the initial condition for the problem, you can see that

$$x_n = x_0 + nh.$$

In figure 5.5, point A has co-ordinates (x_n, y_n) and AB is the line segment whose gradient matches that of the direction field at A. The slope of AB is therefore $f(x_n, y_n)$. Point B has co-ordinates (x_{n+1}, y_{n+1}). The value of y_{n+1} is calculated as follows.

From triangle AA'B,

$$\tan\theta = \frac{A'B}{AA'} = \frac{y_{n+1} - y_n}{h}$$

$$\Rightarrow \quad y_{n+1} = y_n + h\tan\theta$$

But at A, $\quad \tan\theta = \dfrac{dy}{dx} = f(x_n, y_n)$

$$\Rightarrow \quad y_{n+1} = y_n + hf(x_n, y_n).$$

Figure 5.5

This is *Euler's formula*. You can use it to calculate the y values of the solution to the differential equation once you know the initial values of x and y. It is an example of a *step-by-step method* because you proceed one small step at a time to find a solution. For each new step you use the results of the last step. Example 5.1 shows the method in use.

EXAMPLE 5.1

Use Euler's formula to estimate the value at $x = 1$ of the particular solution of the differential equation

$$\frac{dy}{dx} = x^2 + y^2$$

> You saw how to construct a tangent field for this equation on page 22.

which passes through the point $(0, 0.5)$. Use a step length of 0.25.

SOLUTION

It is a good idea to lay out the solution as a table, showing all the calculations that are performed. Table 5.1 shows the results rounded to 4 decimal places.

n	x_n	y_n	$f(x_n, y_n)$	$hf(x_n, y_n)$	$y_{n+1} = y_n + hf(x_n, y_n)$
0	0	0.5	0.25	0.062 5	0.562 5
1	0.25	0.562 5	0.378 9	0.094 7	0.657 2
2	0.5	0.657 2	0.681 9	0.170 5	0.827 7
3	0.75	0.827 7	1.247 6	0.311 9	1.139 6
4	1.0	1.139 6			

Table 5.1

This means the value of y when $x = 1.0$

Euler's numerical method gives the estimate $y(1.0) = 1.1396$.

The calculations involved in Euler's method (as for many other numerical methods) are easily carried out on a spreadsheet. Table 5.2 shows how the spreadsheet might look on the screen (for $h = 0.1$). One advantage of a spreadsheet approach is that you can easily change the step length and generate a new set of values. Consequently it is easy to see how the error is reduced by using a smaller step length.

Spreadsheet for Euler's method					$y' = x^{\wedge 2} + y^{\wedge 2}$
Please input the following variables:					
start for:					
x	0				
y	0.5				
step length (h)	0.1				
n	xn	yn	f(xn, yn)	hf(xn, yn)	yn+1=yn+hf(xn,yn)
0	0	0.5	0.25	0.025	0.525
1	0.1	0.525	0.285625	0.0285625	0.5535625
2	0.2	0.5535625	0.3464314	0.0346431	0.5882056
3	0.3	0.5882056	0.4359859	0.0435986	0.6318042
4	0.4	0.6318042	0.5591766	0.0559177	0.6877219
5	0.5	0.6877219	0.7229614	0.0722961	0.760018
6	0.6	0.760018	0.9376274	0.0937627	0.8537808
7	0.7	0.8537808	1.2189416	0.1218942	0.9756749
8	0.8	0.9756749	1.5919416	0.1591942	1.1348691
9	0.9	1.1348691	2.0979279	0.2097928	1.3446619
10	1	1.3446619	2.8081156	0.2808116	1.6254734

Table 5.2 $f(x_n, y_n) = x_n^2 + y_n^2$; $h = 0.1$

Ten steps of size 0.1 give the answer.

Use a spreadsheet to find, correct to 2 decimal places, the value of y when $x = 1$ for $\dfrac{dy}{dx} = x^2 + y^2$, given that $y = 0.5$ when $x = 0$. The display for $h = 0.1$ should be like the one shown in table 5.2, but you will need then to take smaller steps to achieve the required accuracy.

EXERCISE 5A

Each question gives a differential equation, an initial condition and a step length. Use Euler's method with the given step length, h, to estimate the value of y for the stated value of x. Repeat each solution with smaller step lengths and compare your answers.

1 $\dfrac{dy}{dx} = x - y^2;$ $y = 1$ when $x = 2$.

   Using $h = 0.2$, estimate the value of $y(3)$.

2 $\dfrac{dy}{dx} = \sqrt{x + y};$ $y = 2$ when $x = 1$.

   Using $h = 0.1$, estimate the value of $y(1.4)$.

3 $\dfrac{dy}{dx} = x^2 - y^2;$ $y = 2.1$ when $x = 1.5$.

   Using $h = 0.2$, estimate the value of $y(2.5)$.

4 $\dfrac{dy}{dx} = 2xy + 1;$ $y = 0$ when $x = 0$.

   Using $h = 0.1$, estimate the value of $y(1)$.

Analysing the error

You probably sense that the smaller the step size, the better is the estimate you obtain using Euler's method. You can illustrate this by using Euler's method on a differential equation which has an analytical solution.

Take the simple differential equation $\dfrac{dy}{dx} = y$, with initial condition $y = 1$ when $x = 0$. The analytical solution is $y = e^x$.

The formula for Euler's method is

$$y_{n+1} = y_n + hf(x_n, y_n)$$

Since $f(x, y) = y$ in this case, $f(x_n, y_n) = y_n$.

and in this case this becomes

$$y_{n+1} = y_n + hy_n \quad \text{with } y_0 = 1.$$

Table 5.3 shows the approximations to $y(1)$ obtained using different values of h. It also shows the percentage error calculated for each case using

$$\% \text{ error} = \frac{\text{analytical solution} - \text{numerical solution}}{\text{analytical solution}} \times 100.$$

In this case the analytical solution is known to be $y(1) = e^1 = 2.718\,282$ (to 6 decimal places).

h	Numerical solution	% error	Number of steps
0.1	2.593 742	4.58	10
0.01	2.704 814	0.50	100
0.001	2.716 924	0.05	1000
0.0001	2.718 146	0.005	10 000

Table 5.3

Table 5.3 shows that the accuracy is much increased if you reduce the step size from 0.1 to 0.0001. However, this clearly lengthens the time needed for the calculation: it takes 10 steps of calculation if $h = 0.1$ and 1000 steps if $h = 0.001$. To obtain a sufficiently accurate estimate may require a very small step size, necessitating additional calculations and more computer time.

Of course, the importance of a numerical method is not its use in solving differential equations that can be solved analytically, but in solving differential equations for which analytical methods do not exist. Table 5.4 shows the estimate of $y(1.0)$ obtained by applying Euler's numerical method to the differential equation $\dfrac{dy}{dx} = x^2 + y^2$ (which cannot be solved analytically), with the initial condition $y = 0.5$ when $x = 0$.

h	Estimate of $y(1.0)$
0.2	1.1964
0.125	1.3020
0.1	1.3447
0.0625	1.4185
0.05	1.4463
0.025	1.5081
0.01	1.5498

Table 5.4

It is not possible to do the calculation with a step length of zero, because this would involve an infinite number of calculations. However, were you able to do so, you would expect the answer to be exact, with zero error (ignoring any computer-generated error). You could express this as 'when $h \to 0$, error $\to 0$'.

A graph of the estimate of $y(1.0)$ against h is shown in figure 5.6.

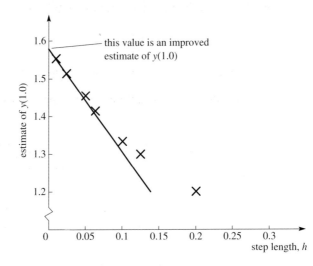

Figure 5.6 *Graph of estimates of y(1.0) for different step lengths*

Figure 5.6 illustrates an important feature of Euler's method. As the step size decreases, the estimates for $y(1.0)$ appear to lie very close to a straight line.

For small values of h the error is approximately a linear function of h.

This provides a useful method of increasing the accuracy for the estimate of y using Euler's method, with little increase in the number of computations or the amount of computer time.

? Look again at the graph in figure 5.6. The straight line that has been drawn is deliberately not a line of best fit. Why not?

EXAMPLE 5.2

You are given the differential equation

$$\frac{dy}{dx} = \frac{y}{x} + 2$$

with initial condition $y = 1$ when $x = 1$.

(i) Estimate the value of $y(2)$ using Euler's method with step size $h = 0.1$ and then with step size $h = 0.05$.

(ii) Use the linear relationship between the error and h in Euler's method to obtain an improved estimate for the value of $y(2)$.

(iii) The analytical solution of the differential equation is $y = x + 2x\ln x$.

Compare your estimate of $y(2)$ in part (ii) with the exact value. Estimate the step size that is required for the basic Euler's method to give an answer correct to 4 decimal places.

SOLUTION

(i) The formula for Euler's method in this case is

$$y_{n+1} = y_n + h\left(\frac{y_n}{x_n} + 2\right)$$

where $x_n = 1 + nh$, with initial conditions $y_0 = 1$ and $x_0 = 1$.

The estimates of $y(2.0)$ obtained using $h = 0.1$ and $h = 0.05$ are shown in table 5.5.

h	Estimate for y(2.0)
0.1	4.675 08
0.05	4.723 21

Table 5.5

(ii) If there is a linear relationship between $y(2)$ and h, then it can be expressed using the straight line equation $y(2) = ah + b$, where a and b are constants. Substituting into this equation the solutions for $h = 0.1$ and $h = 0.05$, you can find values for a and b:

$$4.675\,08 = 0.1a + b$$
$$4.723\,21 = 0.05a + b.$$

Subtracting the second equation from the first,

$$-0.048\,13 = 0.05a,$$

So $a = -0.962\,60$ and $b = 4.771\,33$.

This gives the equation relating $y(2)$ and h as

$$y(2) = 4.771\,33 - 0.9626h.$$

Using this equation you can estimate the exact value of $y(2)$ by putting $h = 0$, giving

$$y(2) = 4.771\,33.$$

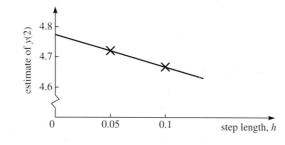

Figure 5.7

(iii) The analytical solution gives $y(2) = 2 + 4\ln2 = 4.772\,58$.

The numerical solution in part (ii) is correct to 2 decimal places. The error in Euler's method is proportional to the step size h, so the error can be expressed as a function of h:

$$y_E - y_N = ch$$

where y_E is the exact solution, y_N is the numerical solution for step size h and c is a constant. Using the solution for $h = 0.05$ and the analytical solution $4.772\,58$, you can find a value for c:

$$4.772\,58 - 4.723\,21 = c \times 0.05$$
$$\Rightarrow \qquad c = 0.987\,398.$$

To obtain an accuracy of 4 decimal places, you require

$$y_E - y_N \leqslant 0.000\,05$$
$$\Rightarrow \qquad ch \leqslant 0.000\,05$$
$$\Rightarrow \qquad h \leqslant \frac{0.000\,05}{0.987\,398}$$
$$\text{i.e.} \qquad h \leqslant 5.1 \times 10^{-5}.$$

This small step size shows that almost 20 000 steps are needed to achieve an accuracy of 4 decimal places.

Note

In the circumstances in which you would use a numerical method you would not know the exact answer. Instead you would estimate your accuracy by looking at the sequence of estimates you had obtained with progressively smaller step lengths. This means that at any stage in the process, the level of accuracy that you have actually achieved is higher than you are able to justify.

In this chapter you have seen Euler's method in action, and seen that the error in the approximate solution can be decreased by reducing the step length. You have also seen that the error is roughly proportional to the step length, providing the step length is small. However, this is only part of the story. It is justifiable to take the error to be proportional to the step length h only when h is small. However, working with small values of h can introduce another source of error if your calculator or computer is working to only a limited number of figures. The area of mathematics that deals with these issues in detail is called *numerical analysis*.

Historical note

Leonard Euler was one of the most prolific and versatile mathematicians ever, his life-time's work amounting to 886 books and papers. Euler was born in Basel in Switzerland in 1707 and as a boy studied under Johann Bernoulli. In 1727 he took the chair of mathematics at St Petersburg Academy in Russia; he later moved to the Prussian Academy in Berlin but returned to St Petersburg for his closing years. He died in 1783 at the age of 76.

Euler's contributions to mathematics are wide-ranging, including the introduction of the symbols f(x), e, $\sum$ and the complex numbers results $e^{jx} = \cos x + j\sin x$ and $e^{j\pi} + 1 = 0$. Much of his work was in applied mathematics including celestial mechanics, hydraulics, ship-building, artillery and music.

EXERCISE 5B

1 This problem is about the differential equation

$$\frac{dy}{dx} = 4x - 0.05y,$$

with the initial condition $y = 80$ when $x = 5$.

(i) Use Euler's numerical method to estimate the value of $y(6)$, using step lengths of 1.0, 0.5, 0.2 and 0.1.

(ii) Illustrate your estimates in part (i) on a graph. Calculate an improved estimate of the value of $y(6)$ as $h \to 0$.

(iii) Use the integrating factor method to find an analytical solution of the differential equation, and hence an exact value of $y(6)$. Compare this with your answer to part (ii).

(iv) Calculate the step size and number of steps needed to obtain an estimate correct to 3 decimal places.

2 This problem is about the differential equation

$$\frac{dy}{dx} = xy^2,$$

with initial condition $y = 0.5$ when $x = 1$.

(i) Use Euler's numerical method to estimate the value of $y(2)$, using step lengths of 0.2, 0.1, 0.05 and 0.01.

(ii) Illustrate your estimates in part (i) on a graph. Calculate an improved estimate of the value of $y(2)$ as $h \to 0$.

(iii) Use the method of separation of variables to find an analytical solution and hence an exact value of $y(2)$. Compare this with your answer to part (ii).

(iv) Calculate the step size and number of steps needed to obtain an estimate correct to 4 decimal places.

3 Using a spreadsheet, estimate to 3 decimal places the value of $y(1)$ for $\frac{dy}{dx} = y + e^{-x}\sin x$ with initial condition $y = 1$ when $x = 0$.

4 Using a spreadsheet, estimate to 3 decimal places the value of $y(1.5)$ for $\frac{dy}{dx} = 1 + x\sin y$ with initial condition $y = 0.5$ when $x = 0$.

5 (i) Use Euler's method with step length 0.1 to estimate the value of $y(1.2)$ given the differential equation

$$\frac{dy}{dx} = x^2 - y^2 \quad (x \geqslant 0)$$

with initial condition $y = 0$ when $x = 1$.

(ii) The table below shows approximate values of $y(1.2)$ for various step lengths.

Step length k	$y(1.2)$
0.01	0.237287
0.005	0.238220
0.002	0.238778
0.001	0.238964

Draw a graph of these approximations to $y(1.2)$ against step length h. What does your graph suggest to you about the relationship between the Euler approximation to $y(1.2)$ and the step length h for small h? Use the graph to estimate the value of $y(1.2)$. How many decimal places can you justify?

6 A car headlight mirror is designed to reflect the light from the headlamp in rays which are parallel to the road surface. In this problem you investigate the required cross-section shape of the headlight mirror. The first diagram shows a geometric model of the situation in which the light rays are emitted from a point source, at the origin.

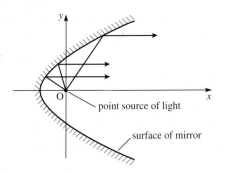

In the second diagram, P is a general point (X, Y) on the curve. The line PQ is the tangent at P, with Q on the x axis. The angle OPQ $= \theta$. The point T is positioned as shown on the x axis. If the mirror is designed correctly, light travelling from the point source at O along OP will be reflected along a horizontal line from P, as shown.

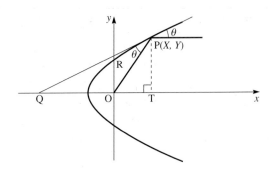

The laws of optics require that the angle of incidence is equal to the angle of reflection. Angle OPQ is the angle of incidence, marked as θ. The angle of reflection has also been marked as θ in the diagram.

(i) Write down the size of angle PQO and hence show that the length OQ is $\sqrt{X^2 + Y^2}$.

(ii) Using triangle QPT, deduce that
$$\tan\theta = \frac{Y}{\sqrt{X^2 + Y^2} + X}.$$

(iii) Hence show that the gradient of the mirror at any point is given by
$$\frac{dy}{dx} = \frac{Y}{\sqrt{x^2 + y^2} + x}.$$

The mirror is designed so that the distance OR of the mirror above the lamp is 6 cm. Taking 1 cm to be 1 unit, this can be written as $y(0) = 6$.

(iv) Use Euler's method to estimate the co-ordinates of several points along the curve.

(v) Use your answers to part (iv) to sketch the curve.

(vi) Verify that $y^2 = 12(x + 3)$ is the analytical solution of the differential equation. Describe the shape of the mirror.

7 The application of Euler's method to solve the differential equation $\frac{dy}{dx} = y^2 - x + 1$ with the initial condition $y = 0$ when $x = 0$, results in the incomplete table below, where the values shown have been rounded to 4 decimal places.

n	x_n	y_n	y'_n	y_{n+1}
0	0	0	1	0.1
1	0.1	0.1	0.91	0.191
2	0.2	0.191	0.8365	0.2746
3	0.3	0.2746	0.7754	0.3522
4	0.4	0.3522	0.7240	0.4246
5	0.5	0.4246	0.6803	
6	0.6			
7	0.7			
8	0.8		0.5818	0.6761
9	0.9	0.6761	0.5571	0.7318
10	1.0	0.7318	0.5355	0.7853

(i) State the value of the step length h used in this case.

(ii) Complete the table by finding values for the remaining entries, giving your answers to 4 decimal places.

(iii) Sketch the graph of y against x, for $0 \leqslant x \leqslant 1$.

(iv) Why does your graph suggest that $y'' < 0$ in the range $0 < x < 1$? If the solution is continued beyond $x = 1$, do you think that $y'' < 0$ will continue to be true? Give reasons for your answer.

(v) If a step length of $h = 0.2$ were used throughout instead, would the solution be more accurate or less accurate, and why?

(vi) Is the *true* value of y at $x = 1.0$ greater or less than the value 0.7318 given in the table? Would your conclusion remain the same if a step length $h = 0.001$ were used instead in a new calculation? Explain your answers briefly.

[MEI]

8 A biologist is researching the population of a species. She tries a number of different models for the rate of growth of the population and solves them to compare with observed data. Her first model is

$$\frac{dp}{dt} = kp\left(1 - \frac{p}{m}\right)$$

where p is the population at time t years, k is a constant and m is the maximum population sustainable by the environment.

(i) Find the general solution of the differential equation.

$$\left[\text{You may use without proof the fact that}\right.$$
$$\left.\frac{1}{p\left(1 - \frac{p}{m}\right)} = \frac{1}{p} + \frac{1}{m - p}.\right]$$

Her observations suggest $k = 0.2$ and $m = 100\,000$.

(ii) If the initial population is 30 000, calculate the population after 5 years.

She decides that this model needs to be refined. She proposes a model

$$\frac{dp}{dt} = kp\left(1 - \left(\frac{p}{m}\right)^{\alpha}\right)$$

and investigates suitable values of α.

(iii) Her observations lead her to the conclusion that the maximum growth rate occurs when the population is 70% of its maximum. By considering the stationary points of the function

$$f(p) = kp\left(1 - \left(\frac{p}{m}\right)^{\alpha}\right)$$

show that $(\alpha + 1)0.7^{\alpha} = 1$.

The biologist solves this equation to get $\alpha \approx 5$. With this value, use Euler's method to calculate values for p. The algorithm is given by $p_{n+1} = p_n + hf(p_n)$ where h is the step length, and $f(p) = \dfrac{dp}{dt}$.

The table shows some values calculated using a step length of 0.2 and the same values of k, m and the initial population as before.

t	p	$\dfrac{dp}{dt}$
0	30 000	5 985.42
0.2	31 917.084	6 220.9788
0.4	32 441.2798	6 464.9419
:	:	:
4.4	69 012.1579	11 641.7855
4.6	71 340.515	

(iv) Continue the table from the last entry to $t = 5$ in order to calculate the population after 5 years.

[MEI]

9 The differential equation $\dfrac{dy}{dx} = \dfrac{1}{\sqrt{x^2 + y^2}}$ is to be investigated, firstly by means of a tangent field and then numerically.

(i) Describe the isocline $\dfrac{dy}{dx} = m$, where m is a positive constant.

(ii) Sketch (using the same axes) the isoclines given by $\dfrac{dy}{dx} = 0.25, 0.5, 1$ and 2. Use these to draw a tangent field for the equation.

(iii) On your tangent field, sketch the solution curves through the points $(0, 1)$, $(1, 0)$ and $(0.5, 0.5)$.

Points on the solution curve through $(0, 1)$ are to be found numerically using Euler's method. The algorithm is given by $x_{n+1} = x_n + h$, $y_{n+1} = y_n + hf(x_n, y_n)$, where h is the step length and $f(x, y) = \dfrac{dy}{dx}$.

(iv) Use a step length of $h = 0.25$ to calculate an approximation for $y(1)$, the value of y when $x = 1$.

(v) The table shows values calculated for $y(1)$ for a succession of smaller step lengths.

h	Approximation for $y(1)$
0.05	1.7066
0.02	1.7006
0.01	1.6986

Assuming that the error in the approximation for $y(1)$ is proportional to h, use the last two entries to find a better estimate for $y(1)$.

[MEI]

10 The differential equation $\dfrac{dy}{dx} = \sqrt{\dfrac{y - x}{x}}$, where $y \geqslant x > 0$, is to be investigated.

(i) Show that the isoclines are given by straight lines through the origin. Sketch (using the same axes) the isoclines $y = x$, $y = 1.5x$, $y = 2x$ and $y = 3x$ for $0 \leqslant x \leqslant 4$ and $0 \leqslant y \leqslant 4$.

(ii) Use the differential equation to calculate the value of $\dfrac{dy}{dx}$ corresponding to each of these isoclines. Hence draw on your diagram a tangent field for the differential equation.

(iii) Sketch on your diagram the solution curves through $(1, 2)$ and $(4, 4)$.

A numerical solution is now sought using Euler's method. The algorithm is given by

$$x_{n+1} = x_n + h, \qquad y_{n+1} = y_n + hf(x_n, y_n),$$

where h is the step length and $f(x, y) = \dfrac{dy}{dx}$.

The algorithm is applied with $h = 0.1$, starting at the point $(1, 2)$. When $x = 3.3$, the calculated value for y is 3.4202.

(iv) Continue the algorithm for two more steps. Can the algorithm be used any further for this curve? Explain your answer.

(v) How could the algorithm be applied to calculate values for the solution curve through $(4, 4)$? Demonstrate your method by applying it for two steps.

[MEI]

11 A bungee jumper of mass $m\,$kg is attached by her ankles to one end of an elastic rope. The other end of the rope is secured to a high bridge. She falls vertically from rest and her displacement below the bridge after t seconds is $x\,$m. Before the rope is taut, the only forces acting on her are her weight and air resistance of magnitude kmv^2, where $v\,$ms^{-1} is her velocity and k is a constant.

It is assumed that in free fall her terminal velocity would be 70 ms^{-1}.

(i) Calculate the value of k and show that, before the rope is taut, v is described by the equation $v\dfrac{dv}{dx} = 9.8 - 0.002v^2$.

State the initial conditions for the equation.

(ii) Solve the differential equation to find v in terms of x. If the unstretched length of the rope is 20 m, show that at the instant when the rope becomes taut, her velocity is 19.41 ms^{-1} (correct to 2 decimal places).

When the rope is taut and she is still moving down, the motion can be described by the equation

$$\frac{dv}{dx} = \frac{9.8 - 0.002v^2 - 1.55(x-20)}{v}.$$

The diagram shows a completed tangent field for $\dfrac{dv}{dx}$ for $x \geqslant 20$. The curve shown for $x \leqslant 20$ is the solution for v found in part (ii).

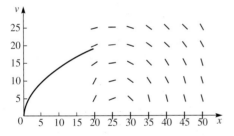

(iii) Sketch the solution curve for $x \geqslant 20$ starting at $(20, 19.41)$. Hence estimate the greatest depth that the bungee jumper reaches below her starting point.

An attempt is made to estimate values of v using Euler's method beginning at $x = 20$, $v = 19.41$ and with a step length of 0.5. The algorithm is given by

$$x_{n+1} = x_n + h, \qquad v_{n+1} = v_n + hf(x_n, v_n)$$

where h is the step length and $f(x, v) = \dfrac{dv}{dx}$.

The algorithm estimates that when $x = 42.5$, $v = 5.74$.

(iv) Continue the algorithm for two more steps. What does this method predict for the greatest depth (to the nearest metre)? Can this algorithm be continued to calculate further values for v? Explain your answer.

[MEI]

12 A pendulum consists of a light rod of length 1 m with a heavy metal disc attached at one end. The other end is fixed to a point about which the pendulum is free to swing. The angle the pendulum makes with the downward vertical at time t is denoted by θ, as shown in the diagram.

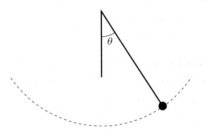

The pendulum swings in a vertical plane and the equation modelling the motion of one swing from $\theta = -\frac{1}{3}\pi$ to $\frac{1}{3}\pi$ is

$$\frac{d\theta}{dt} = \sqrt{g(2\cos\theta - 1)}.$$

The differential equation is to be investigated for this swing of the pendulum, firstly by means of a tangent field and then numerically.

(i) Show that the isoclines are straight lines parallel to the t axis.

(ii) Calculate the (positive) value of $\dfrac{d\theta}{dt}$ for

$\theta = 0, \pm\frac{1}{12}\pi, \pm\frac{1}{6}\pi, \pm\frac{1}{4}\pi$ and $\pm\frac{1}{3}\pi$.

Hence sketch the tangent field for $-\frac{1}{3}\pi < \theta < \frac{1}{3}\pi$ and $-1 < t < 1$.

(iii) On your sketch, draw the solution curves for which
(a) $\theta = 0$ when $t = 0$
(b) $\theta = 0$ when $t = 0.5$.

A numerical solution is to be determined using Euler's method. The algorithm is given by

$$t_{n+1} = t_n + h, \qquad \theta_{n+1} = \theta_n + hf(\theta_n),$$

where h is the step length, and $f(\theta) = \dfrac{d\theta}{dt}$.

(iv) The algorithm is applied from $\theta = 0$, $t = 0$ with a step length of 0.05, and gives an estimate for θ of $\theta = 0.997\,28$ when $t = 0.4$. Continue the algorithm for two more steps and comment on the value of θ obtained.

(v) Explain briefly why this algorithm is not useful when an initial value of $\theta = -\frac{1}{3}\pi$ is taken.

[MEI]

13 The differential equation

$$x\frac{dy}{dx} = y + 2\sqrt{x(y-x)}, \qquad x > 0,$$

is to be investigated numerically using Euler's method. The algorithm is given by

$$x_{r+1} = x_r + h,$$
$$y_{r+1} = y_r + hy'_r,$$

where y'_r is the value of $\dfrac{dy}{dx}$ at (x_r, y_r).

The table shows the solution calculated from the initial conditions $x = 1, y = 2$.

x_r	y_r	y'_r	y_{r+1}
1.0	2	4	2.4
1.1	2.4	4.3560	2.8356
1.2	2.8356	4.6980	3.3054
1.3	3.3054	5.0267	3.8081
1.4	3.8081	5.3431	
1.5			
1.6			
1.7		6.2269	6.1241
1.8	6.1241	6.5021	6.7743
1.9	6.7743	6.7688	7.4512
2.0	7.4512	7.0275	8.1539

(i) Calculate the values for the missing entries in the table.

(ii) Sketch the graph of y against x for $1 \le x \le 2$.

(iii) Explain why the graph suggests that $y'' > 0$. Are the estimates for y overestimates or underestimates? Explain your answer.

The algorithm may be used to generate solutions to this differential equation from different starting points.

(iv) Why will the algorithm fail if at any stage $y_r < x_r$?

(v) Given that $h > 0$, show that if $y_r > x_r > 0$ then $y'_r > 1$, and hence that $y_{r+1} > x_{r+1} > 0$.

[MEI]

14 The solution to the differential equation

$$\frac{dy}{dx} = \sqrt{\frac{1}{25} + x^2 y^2}$$

is to be investigated, first by means of a tangent field and then numerically.

(i) Show that $x = 0$ is an isocline. Show that all other isoclines are of the form $y = \dfrac{a}{x}$.

Solution curves are to be drawn through the points $(-2, 0)$ and $(0, -1)$.

(ii) Sketch sufficient isoclines in order to produce the tangent field and hence sketch the two curves.

A numerical solution is now sought using Euler's method. The algorithm is given by $x_{r+1} = x_r + h, y_{r+1} = y_r + hf(x_r, y_r)$, where $f(x, y) = \dfrac{dy}{dx}$.

(iii) Apply the algorithm for two equal steps, starting from the point $(0, 0)$, to establish the value of y when $x = 0.4$. If the estimate is recalculated with a smaller step length, will the estimate be less or greater? Explain your reasoning.

[MEI]

The modified Euler's method

The modified Euler's method for solving the first order differential equation

$$\frac{dy}{dx} = f(x, y)$$

uses the formula $y_{n+1} = y_n + \frac{1}{2}(k_1 + k_2)$

where $k_1 = hf(x_n, y_n)$ and $k_2 = hf(x_n + h, y_n + k_1)$.

The error in Euler's method is linearly dependent on h. Investigate, by solving several differential equations, each with a range of values of h, how the error in using the modified Euler's method varies with h.

KEY POINTS

1 Euler's numerical step-by-step method for solving the differential equation $\frac{dy}{dx} = f(x, y)$ with initial condition $y = b$ when $x = a$ and a step length h is given by

$$y_{n+1} = y_n + hf(x_n, y_n): \quad y_0 = b$$
$$x_n = a + nh.$$

2 The error in the estimate obtained from the numerical solution is approximately proportional to the step size h for small h.

3 Reducing the step size usually reduces the error.

Linear equations with constant coefficients

As is well-known, Physics became a science only after the invention of differential calculus.

Riemann

 How long does it take a parachutist to reach the ground?

A reasonable model is provided by considering the parachutist as a particle of mass m subject to two forces: weight, mg, and resistance, kv (where v is the speed and k a constant).

Figure 6.1

Applying Newton's second law with the downward direction as positive gives

$$mg - kv = ma. \qquad \qquad ①$$

If the distance fallen is denoted by s, then

$$v = \frac{\mathrm{d}s}{\mathrm{d}t} \text{ and } a = \frac{\mathrm{d}v}{\mathrm{d}t} = \frac{\mathrm{d}^2s}{\mathrm{d}t^2}.$$

So equation ① can be rewritten as

$$mg - k\frac{ds}{dt} = m\frac{d^2s}{dt^2},$$

or

$$\frac{d^2s}{dt^2} + \frac{k}{m}\frac{ds}{dt} = g. \qquad ②$$

Since this contains the term $\frac{d^2s}{dt^2}$, it is a *second order* differential equation.

Higher order equations

So far in this book you have solved only first order equations. In this chapter you will look at second (and higher) order equations. Second order equations are often needed in mechanics, particularly to model situations which (like the one above) involve acceleration.

ACTIVITY

Show that the differential equation ② for the parachutist can be written as

$$\frac{d^2s}{dt^2} + 2\frac{ds}{dt} = 10$$

in the case where, in SI units, $m = 60$, $k = 120$ and $g = 10$.

Given that when $t = 0$, $s = 0$ and $\frac{ds}{dt} = 20$, verify that

$$s = 5t + 7.5(1 - e^{-2t})$$

is the particular solution of this equation.

Classification of differential equations

The differential equation

$$\frac{d^3y}{dx^3} - 7\frac{d^2y}{dx^2} + 2\frac{dy}{dx} + 4y = 3\sin x$$

is described as

* *third order* (because the highest derivative is third order)
* *linear* (because where y appears it is to the power 1: there are no terms involving y^2, $\sqrt{y}$, etc.)
* having *constant coefficients* (because the coefficients of the terms involving y, namely 1, -7, 2 and 4 are all constants)
* *non-homogeneous* (because the right-hand side, the part not containing y, is not zero). In cases when it is zero, the equation ① is called *homogeneous*.

The general second order linear differential equation with constant coefficients may be written as

$$\frac{d^2y}{dx^2} + a\frac{dy}{dx} + by = f(x)$$

where a and b are constant. Although this equation appears quite daunting, it is in fact possible to solve it using a method which does not involve any integration. You will find that such equations arise quite often when you are modelling real situations. For this reason, much of the remainder of this book concentrates on solving second order equations of this type: Chapters 7 and 8 are devoted to a very important context in which they arise – that of *oscillating systems*.

Note

In many other textbooks the terms *homogeneous* and *non-homogeneous* are taken to have a different meaning. The sense in which they are used in this book is now in widespread use.

The first order equation

Before solving second and higher order differential equations you will find it helpful to look at the form of the solution of first order linear, homogeneous differential equations with constant coefficients. The general first order equation of this type can be written as

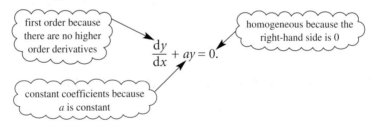

first order because there are no higher order derivatives

homogeneous because the right-hand side is 0

$$\frac{dy}{dx} + ay = 0.$$

constant coefficients because a is constant

You can solve this general differential equation using the method of separation of variables:

$$\frac{dy}{dx} = -ay$$

$$\Rightarrow \quad \int \frac{1}{y} dy = \int -a \, dx$$

$$\Rightarrow \quad \ln |y| = -ax + c \ (c \text{ is a constant of integration}).$$

This gives

$$y = \pm e^{(-ax + c)}$$

$$= A e^{-ax}$$

where $A = \pm e^c$ is a constant.

This shows that the solution of any first order equation of this type will contain an exponential function and an unknown constant.

ACTIVITY Use the method of separation of variables to find the general solution of each of the following differential equations.

(i) $\dfrac{dy}{dx} + 2y = 0$ (iii) $2\dfrac{dy}{dx} - 5y = 0$ (iii) $3\dfrac{dx}{dt} + x = 0$

The auxiliary equation method

Knowing the form of the solution allows you to find it without doing any integration. This is demonstrated in the next example.

EXAMPLE 6.1

Solve the differential equation

$$5\dfrac{dy}{dx} + y = 0.$$

SOLUTION

You begin by assuming an exponential solution of the form

$$y = Ae^{\lambda x},$$

where λ and A are constants.

If this is to be a solution, it must satisfy the differential equation. Differentiating y with respect to x,

$$\dfrac{dy}{dx} = \lambda Ae^{\lambda x}.$$

Substituting this into the differential equation gives

$$5\lambda Ae^{\lambda x} + Ae^{\lambda x} = 0.$$

Dividing both sides by $Ae^{\lambda x}$ gives an equation for λ:

$$5\lambda + 1 = 0.$$

Solving for λ,

$$\lambda = -\dfrac{1}{5}.$$

So the solution of the differential equation is

$$y = Ae^{-\frac{1}{5}x}.$$

 This is in fact the *general* solution of this differential equation. How can you be sure that this is the case and there is not another possible solution?

The equation ① is called the *auxiliary equation* and this method is called the *auxiliary equation* method.

1 Use the auxiliary equation method to find the general solutions of the following differential equations.

(i) $\dfrac{dy}{dx} - 3y = 0$

(ii) $\dfrac{dy}{dx} + 7y = 0$

(iii) $\dfrac{dx}{dt} + x = 0$

(iv) $\dfrac{dp}{dt} - 0.02p = 0$

(v) $5\dfrac{dz}{dt} - z = 0$

2 Use the auxiliary equation method to find the particular solutions of the following differential equations.

(i) $\dfrac{dy}{dx} + 2y = 0$; $y = 3$ when $x = 0$.

(ii) $2\dfrac{dy}{dx} - 5y = 0$; $y = 1$ when $x = 0$.

(iii) $3\dfrac{dx}{dt} + x = 0$; $x = 2$ when $t = 1$.

(iv) $\dfrac{dP}{dt} = kP$; $P = P_0$ when $t = 0$.

(v) $\dfrac{dm}{dt} = -km$; $m = m_0$ when $t = 0$.

3 Find the general solution of the differential equation

$$\dfrac{dy}{dx} + 5y = 0$$

using

(i) the method of separation of variables
(ii) the integrating factor method
(iii) the auxiliary equation method.

Show that in each case the answer can be written in the same form.

4 All of the following differential equations can be solved by at least one of the methods:
- separation of variables
- integrating factor
- auxiliary equation.

In each case state which method (or methods) can be used and use it (or them) to solve the equation.

(i) $\dfrac{dy}{dx} - 17y = 0$

(ii) $\dfrac{dy}{dx} - y^2 = 0$

(iii) $\dfrac{dy}{dx} + xy = 0$

(iv) $\dfrac{dy}{dx} - 3y = 0$

(v) $y\dfrac{dy}{dx} - y^2 = 0$

5 In each case, state what can be said about the function $h(x,y)$ when the differential equation

$$\dfrac{dy}{dx} = h(x,y)$$

can be solved using:

(i) the method of separation of variables
(ii) the integrating factor method
(iii) the auxiliary equation method.

Second order equations

In example 6.1 you developed a method for solving first order equations based on the knowledge that their solutions have exponential form. Can this method be extended to second order equations?

Look at the equation

$$\dfrac{d^2y}{dx^2} - 5\dfrac{dy}{dx} + 6y = 0.$$

Suppose that you assume a solution of the form $y = Ae^{\lambda x}$ where A and λ are constants, then

$$\frac{dy}{dx} = A\lambda e^{\lambda x}$$

and

$$\frac{d^2 y}{dx^2} = A\lambda^2 e^{\lambda x}.$$

Substituting these into the differential equation gives

$$A\lambda^2 e^{\lambda x} - 5A\lambda e^{\lambda x} + 6Ae^{\lambda x} = 0.$$

Dividing through by $Ae^{\lambda x}$, you obtain the quadratic equation in λ,

$$\lambda^2 - 5\lambda + 6 = 0,$$

and this is the *auxiliary equation*. Notice that the form of the auxiliary equation is very close to that of the original differential equation. It could have been written down straight away without any of the intermediate working.

Factorising the auxiliary equation gives

$$(\lambda - 3)(\lambda - 2) = 0.$$

You can see that there are two different values for λ which satisfy the auxiliary equation: $\lambda = 3$ and $\lambda = 2$. So $y = Ae^{3x}$ and $y = Be^{2x}$ (where A and B are constants) are two solutions of the differential equation

$$\frac{d^2 y}{dx^2} - 5\frac{dy}{dx} + 6y = 0.$$

The expressions Ae^{3x} and Be^{2x} are called the *complementary functions* of the differential equation. The sum of these two expressions, $Ae^{3x} + Be^{2x}$, is usually called simply the *complementary function*.

You can now verify that this sum, $y = Ae^{3x} + Be^{2x}$ is also a solution of the second order differential equation.

Differentiating this expression for y gives

$$\frac{dy}{dx} = 3Ae^{3x} + 2Be^{2x}$$

and $\quad \dfrac{d^2 y}{dx^2} = 9Ae^{3x} + 4Be^{2x}.$

Substituting for $\dfrac{d^2 y}{dx^2}, \dfrac{dy}{dx}$ and y, the left-hand side of the original differential equation can now be written as

$$(9Ae^{3x} + 4Be^{2x}) - 5(3Ae^{3x} + 2Be^{2x}) + 6(Ae^{3x} + Be^{2x}).$$

After multiplying out the brackets this becomes

$$9Ae^{3x} + 4Be^{2x} - 15Ae^{3x} - 10Be^{2x} + 6Ae^{3x} + 6Be^{2x},$$

and you can see by collecting like terms that this is equal to zero for all x. So $y = Ae^{3x} + Be^{2x}$ is indeed a solution and this is in fact the general solution.

The method used in this example is one that can be used on any linear equation with constant coefficients, whatever its order. If $\lambda_1, \lambda_2, \lambda_3, \ldots$ are the roots of the auxiliary equation, then, assuming there are no repeated roots, the general solution of the homogeneous differential equation is

$$y = Ae^{\lambda_1 x} + Be^{\lambda_2 x} + Ce^{\lambda_3 x} + \ldots$$

This is an example of the *principle of superposition*. If $u(x)$, $v(x)$, $w(x)$, ... are solutions of a linear differential equation, then the general solution is

$$y = Au + Bv + Cw + \ldots$$

where A, B, C, ... are arbitrary constants. The function y is said to be a *linear combination* of the functions u, v, w, ...

The principle of superposition applies to any homogeneous differential equation with constant coefficients. The following example illustrates the method for a fourth order differential equation.

EXAMPLE 6.2

Solve the differential equation

$$\frac{d^4y}{dx^4} - 2\frac{d^3y}{dx^3} - \frac{d^2y}{dx^2} + 2\frac{dy}{dx} = 0.$$

SOLUTION

You can go straight to the auxiliary equation:

$$\lambda^4 - 2\lambda^3 - \lambda^2 + 2\lambda = 0$$

Factorising this quartic equation gives

$$\lambda(\lambda - 1)(\lambda + 1)(\lambda - 2) = 0.$$

This means that there are four possible roots for λ: $\lambda = 0$, $\lambda = 1$, $\lambda = 1$, $\lambda = 2$.

The general solution is

$$y = A + Be^{-x} + Ce^x + De^{2x}$$

in which A, B, C and D are constants.

There are three important points to notice from example 6.2:

- the method does not involve any integration
- the number of complementary functions is equal to the order of the differential equation
- the number of unknown constants in the solution is equal to the order of the differential equation.

Find the general solution of each of the following differential equations.

1 $\dfrac{d^2y}{dx^2} - 3\dfrac{dy}{dx} + 2y = 0$

2 $6\dfrac{d^2y}{dx^2} + 5\dfrac{dy}{dx} + y = 0$

3 $2\dfrac{d^2y}{dx^2} + \dfrac{dy}{dx} - y = 0$

4 $\dfrac{d^2y}{dx^2} + 4\dfrac{dy}{dx} - 5y = 0$

5 $\dfrac{d^2y}{dx^2} - 4y = 0$

6 $\dfrac{d^3y}{dx^3} - 6\dfrac{d^2y}{dx^2} + 11\dfrac{dy}{dx} - 6y = 0$

7 $\dfrac{d^2x}{dt^2} + \dfrac{dx}{dt} - 6x = 0$

8 $\dfrac{d^2x}{dt^2} - 9x = 0$

9 $\dfrac{d^2u}{dt^2} - 3\dfrac{du}{dt} = 0$

10 $m\dfrac{d^2x}{dt^2} - kx = 0$

where m and k are positive constants.

Finding the values of the unknown constants

The general solution of a second order differential equation contains two unknown constants. To find the values of these constants you need two extra pieces of information. (Remember that for first order equations you needed one extra piece of information.) The extra information is given in one of two different ways.

Initial conditions

If the two pieces of information are given for the same value of the independent variable, you say that you have two *initial conditions*.

For example, $y = 2$ at $x = 1$ and $\dfrac{dy}{dx} = 3$ at $x = 1$ are initial conditions (at $x = 1$).

Problems consisting of a differential equation and initial conditions are called *initial value problems*.

Boundary conditions

If the information is given at two values of the independent variable, you say that you have two *boundary conditions*.

For example, $y = 2$ at $x = 1$ and $y = 1$ at $x = 3$ are boundary conditions (at $x = 1$ and $x = 3$). Problems consisting of a differential equation and two boundary conditions are called *boundary value problems*. In applications which involve boundary value problems the solution is often restricted to the region between the boundary points.

Examples 6.3 and 6.4 show how to use initial and boundary conditions to find the unknown constants.

EXAMPLE 6.3

(i) Find the particular solution of

$$\frac{d^2y}{dx^2} + 4\frac{dy}{dx} + 3y = 0$$

given the initial conditions $y = 0$ and $\frac{dy}{dx} = 1$ at $x = 0$.

(ii) Sketch the graph of the solution.

SOLUTION

(i) The auxiliary equation is $\lambda^2 + 4\lambda + 3 = 0$, which has roots $\lambda = -3$ and $\lambda = -1$. The general solution of the differential equation is

$$y = Ae^{-x} + Be^{-3x}.$$

The first initial condition says that when $x = 0$, $y = 0$, so substituting these into the general solution gives

$$A + B = 0. \qquad \qquad ①$$

Differentiating the general solution gives

$$\frac{dy}{dx} = -Ae^{-x} - 3Be^{-3x}.$$

The second initial condition requires that when $x = 0$, $\frac{dy}{dx} = 1$. Substituting these values into the expression for $\frac{dy}{dx}$ gives

$$-A - 3B = 1. \qquad \qquad ②$$

Solving equations ① and ② gives $A = \frac{1}{2}$ and $B = -\frac{1}{2}$.

The particular solution is $y = \frac{1}{2}e^{-x} - \frac{1}{2}e^{-3x}$.

(ii) The graph of y is shown in figure 6.2. Both of the terms $\frac{1}{2}e^{-x}$ and $-\frac{1}{2}e^{-3x}$ decay to zero with increasing x.

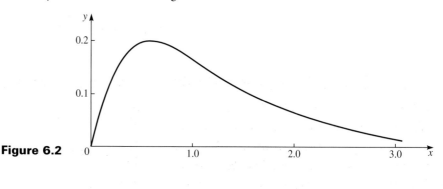

Figure 6.2

EXAMPLE 6.4

The differential equation

$$\frac{d^2y}{dx^2} + 4\frac{dy}{dx} + 3y = 0.$$

> Notice that this is the same differential equation as in example 6.3.

is used to model a situation in which the value of x lies between 0 and 2.

(i) Find the particular solution given the boundary conditions $y = 0$ when $x = 0$ and $y = 1$ when $x = 2$.

(ii) Sketch a graph of the solution for $0 \leqslant x \leqslant 2$.

SOLUTION

(i) The general solution is

$$y = Ae^{-x} + Be^{-3x}$$

as before.

Using the boundary conditions:

when $x = 0$, $y = 0 \Rightarrow A + B = 0$ ①

when $x = 2$, $y = 1 \Rightarrow Ae^{-2} + Be^{-6} = 1$.   ②

Substituting for B from ① into ② gives

$$Ae^{-2} - Ae^{-6} = 1$$

$$A = \frac{e^2}{1 - e^{-4}}$$

and also $B = -\dfrac{e^2}{1 - e^{-4}}$.

The particular solution in this case is

$$y = \frac{e^2}{1 - e^{-4}}(e^{-x} - e^{-3x}).$$

(ii) Figure 6.3 shows the values of y for the given range of values of x.

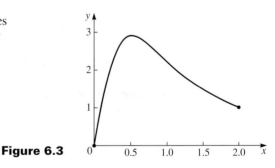

Figure 6.3

EXERCISE 6C

Find the particular solution of each of the differential equations in questions 1–5, and illustrate it with a sketch graph. Use a graphics calculator or a computer to check your answers. Describe the shape of the graph as the independent variable increases.

1 $\dfrac{d^2y}{dx^2} - 5\dfrac{dy}{dx} + 6y = 0$; initial conditions $y = 1$

and $\dfrac{dy}{dx} = 0$ when $x = 0$.

2 $\dfrac{d^2y}{dx^2} - 9y = 0$; initial conditions $y = 0$ and

$\dfrac{dy}{dx} = 1$ when $x = 0$.

3 $\dfrac{d^2x}{dt^2} + 6\dfrac{dx}{dt} + 5x = 0$; boundary conditions $x = 0$

when $t = 0$ and $x = 2$ when $t = 1$.

4 $\dfrac{d^2v}{dt^2} - v = 0$; boundary conditions $v = -1$ when

$t = -1$ and $v = 1$ when $t = 1$.

5 $\dfrac{d^2y}{dx^2} - 5\dfrac{dy}{dx} = 0$; initial conditions $y = 0$ and

$\dfrac{dy}{dx} = 4$ when $x = 0$.

6 The metal fins on a motor cycle engine help to cool it. A model for the change of temperature along a fin is given by

$$\frac{d^2T}{dx^2} - 4T = 0$$

where $T°C$ is the temperature and x m is the distance from the hot end.

(i) Find the general solution of this differential equation.

When the engine has been running for some time the temperatures at the two ends of the fin are 100°C and 80°C. The fin is 5 cm long.

(ii) Find the particular solution.

(iii) Hence determine the temperature 3 cm from the hot end.

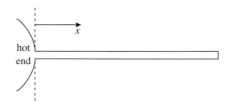

Auxiliary equation with complex roots: pure imaginary roots

The auxiliary equation for a second order differential equation is a quadratic equation in λ. So far you have only seen cases in which the roots of the auxiliary equation were real and distinct numbers λ_1 and λ_2. The general solution of these differential equations had the form

$$y = Ae^{\lambda_1 x} + Be^{\lambda_2 x}.$$

However, the auxiliary equation does not always have real roots. For example, the differential equation

$$\frac{d^2y}{dx^2} + 4y = 0 \qquad \text{①}$$

has auxiliary equation

$$\lambda^2 + 4 = 0.$$

You can see that this has no real roots. The roots of the equation are the complex numbers $\lambda_1 = 2j$ and $\lambda_2 = -2j$ (where $j = \sqrt{-1}$).

 You will see i used instead of j for $\sqrt{-1}$ in some texts.

The general solution of differential equation ① is therefore

$$y = Ae^{2jx} + Be^{-2jx}.$$

Complex exponentials can be written in terms of cosine and sine functions using the relationships

$$e^{j\theta} = \cos\theta + j\sin\theta$$
$$e^{-j\theta} = \cos\theta - j\sin\theta$$

(An explanation of this is given in *Pure Mathematics 5* in this series.)

The general solution can therefore be written as

$$y = A(\cos 2x + j\sin 2x) + B(\cos 2x - j\sin 2x)$$
$$= (A + B)\cos 2x + (jA - jB)\sin 2x.$$

Since A and B are simply unknown constants, you can define new constants C and D such that $A + B = C$ and $jA - jB = D$. The general solution of the original differential equation

$$\frac{d^2y}{dx^2} + 4y = 0$$

can then be written simply as

$$y = C\cos 2x + D\sin 2x.$$

From now on we write this as

$$y = A\sin 2x + B\cos 2x$$

(which simply means that we have renamed the constants).

You can verify that this is the general solution by differentiating y and substituting the resulting expressions into the differential equation.

$$\frac{dy}{dx} = 2A\cos 2x - 2B\sin 2x$$

$$\frac{d^2y}{dx^2} = -4A\sin 2x - 4B\cos 2x.$$

Substitution into the left-hand side of the differential equation gives

$$(-4A\sin 2x - 4B\cos 2x) + 4(A\sin 2x + B\cos 2x).$$

By collecting like terms you will see that this is zero for all values of x, so $y = A\sin 2x + B\cos 2x$ satisfies the differential equation.

ACTIVITIES

1 Show that substituting $j\theta$ for x in the expansion

$$e^x = 1 + x + \frac{x^2}{2!} + \frac{x^3}{3!} + \ldots + \frac{x^r}{r!} \ldots$$

gives $e^{j\theta} = \cos\theta + j\sin\theta$.

2 Show **(i)** by verification, and **(ii)** using the auxiliary equation method, that the general solution of the differential equation

$$\frac{d^2x}{dt^2} + \omega^2 x = 0$$

is $x = A\sin\omega t + B\cos\omega t$.

Oscillating solutions

In cases where the auxiliary equation has real roots, the solution involves either exponential growth or exponential decay, as shown in figure 6.4.

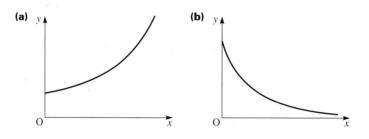

Figure 6.4 *Typical solution curves for y = Ae^{λx} (where λ is real and A > 0); real λ:* **(a)** *λ > 0* **(b)** *λ < 0*

However when the auxiliary equation has complex roots, sine and cosine terms are introduced into the solution and this means that it will involve oscillations. This is illustrated in examples 6.5 and 6.6

EXAMPLE 6.5

Find the particular solution of the differential equation

$$\frac{d^2y}{dx^2} + 16y = 0$$

that satisfies the initial conditions $y = 0$ and when $x = 0$.

SOLUTION

The auxiliary equation is

$$\lambda^2 + 16 = 0.$$

and this has roots $\lambda_1 = 4j$ and $\lambda_2 = -4j$.

The general solution of the differential equation is therefore

$$y = A\sin4x + B\cos4x.$$

> Notice that you go straight to the sine and cosine form.

When $x = 0$, $y = 0 \Rightarrow B = 0$.

The solution becomes $y = A\sin4x$.

Differentiating this solution with respect to x gives

$$\frac{dy}{dx} = 4A\cos4x.$$

When $x = 0$, $\frac{dy}{dx} = 2 \Rightarrow 4A = 2$

$$\Rightarrow A = \tfrac{1}{2}.$$

The particular solution is $y = \frac{1}{2}\sin 4x$. Figure 6.5 shows a graph of the particular solution. You will notice that the solution curve is oscillatory.

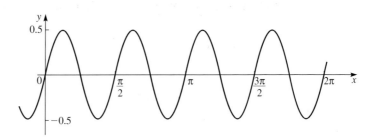

Figure 6.5

Auxiliary equation with complex roots: the general case

In examples 6.4 and 6.5 the auxiliary equations

$$\lambda^2 + 4 = 0 \text{ and } \lambda^2 + 16 = 0$$

both had pure imaginary roots, $\pm 2j$ and $\pm 4j$ respectively.

However, many differential equations give rise to auxiliary equations with roots that are part real and part imaginary, as in the next example.

EXAMPLE 6.6

Find the particular solution of the differential equation

$$\frac{d^2y}{dx^2} + 2\frac{dy}{dx} + 5y = 0$$

which satisfies the initial conditions $y = 0$ and $\dfrac{dy}{dx} = 1$ when $x = 0$.

SOLUTION

The auxiliary equation is

$$\lambda^2 + 2\lambda + 5 = 0.$$

Solving for λ, using the quadratic formula (since the equation cannot be factorised):

$$\lambda = \frac{-2 \pm \sqrt{4 - 20}}{2} = -1 \pm 2j.$$

The general solution is

$$y = Pe^{(-1 + 2j)x} + Qe^{(-1 - 2j)x}$$
$$= e^{-x}(Pe^{2jx} + Qe^{-2jx})$$

and since $Pe^{2jx} + Qe^{-2jx}$ can be written as $A\sin 2x + B\cos 2x$,

$$y = e^{-x}(A\sin 2x + B\cos 2x).$$

Substituting the initial condition, when $x = 0$, $y = 0$, into the general solution gives $B = 0$. So the solution is now

$$y = Ae^{-x}\sin2x.$$

Differentiating with respect to x gives

$$\frac{dy}{dx} = -Ae^{-x}\sin2x + 2Ae^{-x}\cos2x.$$

Substituting the other initial condition, when $x = 0$, $\frac{dy}{dx} = 1$, into this equation gives

$$2A = 1$$

$$\Rightarrow \quad A = \frac{1}{2}.$$

The particular solution for these initial conditions is

$$y = \frac{1}{2}e^{-x}\sin2x.$$

The graph of this particular solution is shown in figure 6.6.

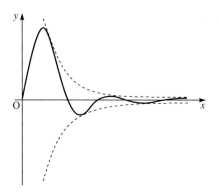

Figure 6.6

Notice the relationship between the algebraic solution, $y = \frac{1}{2}e^{-x}\sin2x$, and its graph. The factor e^{-x} tells you that it is subject to exponential decay because of the negative sign in the power; the factor $\sin2x$ tells you that there is an oscillation. So just by looking at the algebraic expression you can say that the form of the solution is an exponentially decaying oscillation. This form of solution arises frequently when you are modelling real oscillating systems.

? (i) How would you sketch the curve $y = e^{2x}\cos3x$ without plotting points or using a graphics calculator?

(ii) What auxiliary equation would give rise to such a solution?

For each of the differential equations in questions 1–5, find the particular solution which corresponds to the given conditions and draw a sketch graph of the solution. Assuming these differential equations are models for real systems, use your graph to describe the motion of each system.

1 $\dfrac{d^2x}{dt^2} + 9x = 0$; initial conditions $x = 0$ and

$\dfrac{dx}{dt} = 1$ when $t = 0$.

2 $4\dfrac{d^2x}{dt^2} + x = 0$; initial conditions $x = 4$ and

$\dfrac{dx}{dt} = 0$ when $t = 0$.

3 $\dfrac{d^2x}{dt^2} + 4x = 0$; boundary conditions $x = 1$ when

$t = \dfrac{\pi}{4}$ and $x = 0$ when $t = \dfrac{\pi}{2}$.

4 $\dfrac{d^2x}{dt^2} + 12x = 0$; boundary conditions $x = 0$

when $t = 0$ and $x = 3$ when $t = 1$.

5 $m\dfrac{d^2x}{dt^2} + kx = 0$; (where m and k are positive

constants); initial conditions $x = 0$ and $\dfrac{dx}{dt} = 1$

when $t = 0$.

6 Find the general solution of each of the following differential equations.

(i) $\dfrac{d^2y}{dx^2} - 4\dfrac{dy}{dx} + 5y = 0$

(ii) $\dfrac{d^2y}{dx^2} - 2\dfrac{dy}{dx} + 5y = 0$

(iii) $\dfrac{d^2x}{dt^2} + 2\dfrac{dx}{dt} + 4x = 0$

(iv) $4\dfrac{d^2x}{dt^2} + 4\dfrac{dx}{dt} + 5x = 0$

7 Find the particular solution of each of the following equations for the conditions given. Use a graphics calculator or computer to graph the solution. Describe the shape of the graph as the independent variable increases.

(i) $\dfrac{d^2y}{dx^2} + 2\dfrac{dy}{dx} + 2y = 0$; $y = 0$ and $\dfrac{dy}{dx} = 2$

when $x = 0$.

(ii) $4\dfrac{d^2y}{dx^2} - 8\dfrac{dy}{dx} + 5y = 0$; $y = 2$ and $\dfrac{dy}{dx} = 0$

when $x = 0$.

(iii) $\dfrac{d^2y}{dx^2} + 2\dfrac{dy}{dx} + 5y = 0$; $y = 0$ when $x = 0$ and

$y = 3$ when $x = \dfrac{\pi}{4}$.

(iv) $\dfrac{d^2x}{dt^2} - 3\dfrac{dx}{dt} + 4x = 0$; $\dfrac{dx}{dt} = 0$ and $x = 1$

when $t = 0$.

Auxiliary equation with repeated roots

Look at the second order differential equation:

$$\frac{d^2y}{dx^2} - 4\frac{dy}{dx} + 4y = 0.$$

Assuming a solution of the form $y = Ae^{\lambda x}$, you obtain the auxiliary equation

$$\lambda^2 - 4\lambda + 4 = 0$$
$$\Rightarrow (\lambda - 2)^2 = 0.$$

This auxiliary equation is a special case: it has 2 as a repeated root, so it has only one root, $\lambda = 2$. This gives you only one complementary function Ae^{2x}. But since the equation was of second order, you expect the auxiliary equation to have two roots, giving a general solution with two unknown constants.

To find such a solution, try replacing the simple form Ae^{2x} with the more general form $f(x)e^{2x}$, and investigate the form of the function $f(x)$.

Differentiating this solution gives

$$\frac{dy}{dx} = 2e^{2x}f + e^{2x}\frac{df}{dx}.$$

Using the product rule.
Notice that for simplicity
$f(x)$ is now written as just f.

Differentiating again gives

$$\frac{d^2y}{dx^2} = 4e^{2x}f + 4e^{2x}\frac{df}{dx} + e^{2x}\frac{d^2f}{dx^2}.$$

Substituting these expressions into the differential equation gives

$$\left(e^{2x}\frac{d^2f}{dx^2} + 4e^{2x}\frac{df}{dx} + 4e^{2x}f\right) - 4\left(e^{2x}\frac{df}{dx} + 2e^{2x}f\right) + 4e^{2x}f = 0.$$

This simplifies to

$$e^{2x}\frac{d^2f}{dx^2} + (4e^{2x} - 4e^{2x})\frac{df}{dx} + (4e^{2x} - 8e^{2x} + 4e^{2x})f = 0.$$

The coefficients of the terms in f and $\frac{df}{dx}$ are zero, so you are left with

$$\frac{d^2f}{dx^2} = 0.$$

Integrating twice gives

$$f = A + Bx$$

where A and B are unknown constants, showing that the general solution has the form

$$y = (A + Bx)e^{2x}.$$

This is an important result. If $\lambda = \alpha$ is a repeated root of the auxiliary equation, you may assume that the general solution is of the form

$$y = Ae^{\alpha x} + Bxe^{\alpha x}.$$

EXAMPLE 6.7

Find the general solution of the equation

$$\frac{d^2z}{dt^2} - 6\frac{dz}{dt} + 9z = 0.$$

SOLUTION

Assuming a general solution of the form $z = Ae^{\lambda t}$ gives the auxiliary equation

$$\lambda^2 - 6\lambda + 9 = 0$$
$$\Rightarrow \quad (\lambda - 3)^2 = 0$$
$$\Rightarrow \quad \lambda = 3 \text{ (twice)}.$$

The general solution is

$$z = Ae^{3t} + Bte^{3t} = (A + Bt)e^{3t}.$$

ACTIVITY   Find the general solution of the differential equation

$$\frac{d^3y}{dx^3} - 3\alpha\frac{d^2y}{dx^2} + 3\alpha^2\frac{dy}{dx} - \alpha^3y = 0$$

whose auxiliary equation is $(\lambda - \alpha)^3 = 0$.

1 Find the general solution of each of the following differential equations.

(i) $\quad\dfrac{d^2y}{dx^2} - 16y = 0$

(ii) $\quad\dfrac{d^2x}{dt^2} + \omega^2x = 0$ where ω is constant.

(iii) $\quad\dfrac{d^2y}{dx^2} + \dfrac{dy}{dx} - 5y = 0$

(iv) $\quad 3\dfrac{d^2x}{dt^2} + \dfrac{dx}{dt} + 2x = 0$

(v) $\quad\dfrac{d^2y}{dx^2} - 8\dfrac{dy}{dx} + 16y = 0$

(vi) $\quad 2\dfrac{d^2x}{dt^2} + 4\dfrac{dx}{dt} + x = 0$

(vii) $\quad 7\dfrac{d^2y}{dx^2} + 2\dfrac{dy}{dx} = 0$

(viii) $\quad 9\dfrac{d^2y}{dx^2} - 12\dfrac{dy}{dx} + 4y = 0$

(ix) $\quad m\dfrac{d^2x}{dt^2} + r\dfrac{dx}{dt} + kx = 0$ where m, r, and k are constant.

(x) $\quad\dfrac{d^4x}{dt^4} - 16x = 0$

2 Show that if a, b and c are positive constants, then both complementary functions of

$$a\frac{d^2x}{dt^2} + b\frac{dx}{dt} + cx = 0$$

approach zero as t tends to infinity.

3 Find the particular solution in each of the following differential equations, then use a graphics calculator or computer to draw a graph of the solution. Assuming that these differential equations are models for real systems, use your graph to describe the motion of each system.

(i) $\quad\dfrac{d^2x}{dt^2} + 8x = 0$; $x = 1$ and $\dfrac{dx}{dt} = 1$ when $t = 0$.

(ii) $\quad\dfrac{d^2x}{dt^2} + 5\dfrac{dx}{dt} = 0$; $x = 0$ and $\dfrac{dx}{dt} = 4$ when $t = 0$.

(iii) $\quad\dfrac{d^2x}{dt^2} - \dfrac{dx}{dt} + x = 0$; $x = 1$ and $\dfrac{dx}{dt} = 0$ when $t - 0$.

4 For each of the following differential equations, find the particular solution that fits the given conditions.

(i) $\quad\dfrac{d^2y}{dx^2} + 2\dfrac{dy}{dx} + y = 0$; $y = 0$ when $x = 0$ and $y = 2$ when $x = 1$.

(ii) $\quad\dfrac{d^2x}{dt^2} - 6\dfrac{dx}{dt} + 9x = 0$; $x = 1$ and $\dfrac{dx}{dt} = 0$ when $t = 0$.

(iii) $\quad 4\dfrac{d^2x}{dt^2} + 4\dfrac{dx}{dt} + x = 0$; $x = 4$ when $t = 0$ and $x = 0$ when $t = 2$.

(iv) $\quad\dfrac{d^2y}{dx^2} + 2k\dfrac{dy}{dx} + k^2y = 0$; $y = 0$ and $\dfrac{dy}{dx} = 2$ when $x = 0$.

Non-homogeneous equations

You have seen that equations of the form

$$\frac{d^2y}{dx^2} + a\frac{dy}{dx} + by = 0,$$

have the general solution

$$y = Au(x) + Bv(x)$$

where u(x) and v(x) may involve exponential and/or trigonometric functions (and possibly a factor x). In modelling real situations, equations like this often arise in which the right-hand side is non-zero. You then have a *non-homogeneous* linear equation,

$$\frac{d^2y}{dx^2} + a\frac{dy}{dx} + by = f(x).$$

There are many situations in which these equations arise, such as the parachutist example on page 70. One important application is in modelling forced oscillations, and this is discussed in Chapter 8.

As a first step, look at the first order non-homogeneous linear differential equation

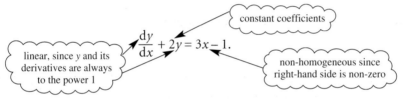

linear, since y and its derivatives are always to the power 1

constant coefficients

$$\frac{dy}{dx} + 2y = 3x - 1.$$

non-homogeneous since right-hand side is non-zero

You have seen how to solve this using the integrating factor method. For this equation the integrating factor is e^{2x} so the equation becomes

$$e^{2x}\frac{dy}{dx} + 2e^{2x}y = (3x - 1)e^{2x}$$

$$\Rightarrow \qquad \frac{d}{dx}(e^{2x}y) = e^{2x}(3x - 1)$$

$$\Rightarrow e^{2x}y = \int e^{2x}(3x - 1)dx.$$

Integrating the right-hand side by parts gives

$$e^{2x}y = \frac{3}{2}xe^{2x} - \frac{5}{4}e^{2x} + A$$

where A is the constant of integration, so

$$y = Ae^{-2x} + \left(\frac{3}{2}x - \frac{5}{4}\right).$$

Notice that the solution consists of two distinct parts.

- The first part, Ae^{-2x}, contains an arbitrary constant, A, and satisfies the homogeneous equation, $\frac{dy}{dx} + 2y = 0$. It is the complementary function of the equation formed by replacing the right-hand side with zero.

- The second part $\left(\frac{3}{2}x - \frac{5}{4}\right)$ includes no arbitrary constants.

This suggests that part of the solution depends only on the left-hand side of the differential equation, and part on the full equation. To explore this idea further, look carefully at the next example which has the same left-hand side as the previous one, but a different right-hand side.

EXAMPLE 6.8

Use the integrating factor method to find the general solution of the first order linear differential equation $\dfrac{dy}{dx} + 2y = e^{3x}$.

SOLUTION

The integrating factor is again e^{2x} so the general solution is given by

$$e^{2x}\frac{dy}{dx} + 2e^{2x}y = e^{2x}e^{3x}$$

$$\Rightarrow \qquad \frac{d}{dx}(ye^{2x}) = e^{5x}$$

$$\Rightarrow \qquad ye^{2x} = \int e^{5x}dx$$

$$= \tfrac{1}{5}e^{5x} + A$$

where A is the constant of integration.

Dividing through by e^{2x}, the general solution is

$$y = \tfrac{1}{5}e^{3x} + Ae^{-2x}.$$

This has the same form, a complementary function Ae^{-2x} and another part, in this case $\tfrac{1}{5}e^{3x}$, which contains no arbitrary constants.

Now look at the two equations and their solutions.

$$\frac{dy}{dx} + 2y = 3x - 1 \qquad \Rightarrow \qquad y = Ae^{-2x} + \tfrac{3}{2}x - \tfrac{5}{4}$$

$$\frac{dy}{dx} + 2y = e^{3x} \qquad \Rightarrow \qquad y = Ae^{-2x} + \tfrac{1}{5}e^{3x}.$$

The complementary function is the same in each case, and could have been found by solving the corresponding homogeneous equation. The other part is the same sort of function as the right-hand side of the differential equation. This function is called the *particular integral*.

ACTIVITY

Verify that in each case the particular integral is a solution of the full differential equation.

In both cases we solved the differential equations using the integrating factor method, but the form of the solutions suggested that another method might be available, one that involves no integration. The outstanding question is how to find a particular integral.

The first step is to write down a suitable trial function. The form of this trial function will be determined by the right-hand side of the differential equation. As an example, take the last differential equation and use ce^{3x} as a trial function. Since you know the solution of this differential equation, you expect c to turn out to be $\frac{1}{5}$.

Substituting $y = ce^{3x}$ and $\dfrac{dy}{dx} = 3ce^{3x}$ into the full differential equation yields

$$3ce^{3x} + 2ce^{3x} = e^{3x}$$
$$\Rightarrow \quad 5ce^{3x} = e^{3x}$$
$$\Rightarrow \quad c = \tfrac{1}{5}.$$

The particular integral is $\frac{1}{5}e^{3x}$, as before.

The method that you have developed may now be summarised as follows.

To solve an equation of the form

$$\frac{dy}{dx} + ay = f(x),$$

1 find the complementary function for the associated homogeneous equation

$$\frac{dy}{dx} + ay = 0$$

2 find, by using a suitable trial function, a particular integral (that is *any* solution of the full differential equation)

3 the general solution of the equation is now found by adding the complementary function and the particular integral together:

general solution = complementary function + particular integral.

When applied to first order equations this method may be thought of as being an alternative to the integrating factor method. However it is much more powerful than that because, unlike the integrating factor method, it can be applied to second and higher order equations as well. This is shown in the next example.

EXAMPLE 6.9

Given the differential equation

$$\frac{d^2y}{dx^2} - 2\frac{dy}{dx} - 3y = 6e^{2x},$$

(i) find the complementary function
(ii) use the function ce^{2x} as a trial function to find a particular integral
(iii) write down the general solution of the differential equation.

SOLUTION

(i) The corresponding homogeneous differential equation is

$$\frac{d^2y}{dx^2} - 2\frac{dy}{dx} - 3y = 0.$$

The auxiliary equation for this differential equation is

$$\lambda^2 - 2\lambda - 3 = (\lambda - 3)(\lambda + 1) = 0.$$

The complementary function is therefore $Ae^{3x} + Be^{-x}$.

(ii) If $y = ce^{2x}$, then $\dfrac{dy}{dx} = 2ce^{2x}$ and $\dfrac{d^2y}{dx^2} = 4ce^{2x}$.

Substituting these into the full differential equation:

$$4ce^{2x} - 2(2ce^{2x}) - 3(ce^{2x}) = 6e^{2x}$$

$$\Rightarrow \qquad\qquad -3ce^{2x} = 6e^{2x}$$

$$\Rightarrow \qquad\qquad c = -2.$$

The particular integral is $-2e^{2x}$.

(iii) The general solution is the complementary function plus the particular integral:

$$y = Ae^{3x} + Be^{-x} - 2e^{2x}.$$

Notice that the general solution given in part (iii) of example 6.9 has the properties you would expect:

- it satisfies the differential equation
- the number of arbitrary constants is the same as the order of the equation, in this case two.

Finding particular integrals

As you have seen in the examples, to find the complementary function for a non-homogenous equation you use the same technique as for the corresponding homogeneous equation. To find a particular integral you need to establish a trial function whose form depends on the form of f(x).

 Look at the following three non-homogeneous differential equations.

(i) $\dfrac{d^2y}{dx^2} + 3\dfrac{dy}{dx} + 2y = x^2 + x - 1$

(ii) $\dfrac{d^2y}{dx^2} + 3\dfrac{dy}{dx} + 2y = \sin 4x - \cos 4x$

(iii) $\dfrac{d^2y}{dx^2} + 3\dfrac{dy}{dx} + 2y = 4e^{-0.5x}$

In each case the complementary function is $Ae^{-x} + Be^{-2x}$.

Suggest a trial function for the particular integral in each case.

You have seen that for a differential equation in which the right-hand side is f(x),

- when f(x) is a linear function, the particular integral is also a linear function
- when f(x) is a trigonometric function, the particular integral is also a trigonometric function
- when f(x) is an exponential function, the particular integral is also an exponential function.

These observations lead us to use trial functions as given in the following table.

Function (x)	Trial function
linear function	$lx + m$
polynomial of order n	$a_n x^n + a_{n-1} x^{n-1} + \ldots + a_1 x + a_0$
trigonometric function involving $\sin px$ and $\cos px$	$l\sin px + m\cos px$
exponential function involving e^{px}	ce^{px}.

Note

This method finds the simplest form of a particular integral and this is sometimes called *the* particular integral. Other expressions for a particular integral may be found by adding on multiples of the terms in the complementary function.

The following examples demonstrate how the approach works for a variety of second order equations.

EXAMPLE 6.10

Find a particular integral of the differential equation

$$\frac{d^2y}{dx^2} + 3\frac{dy}{dx} + 2y = 4x - 1.$$

SOLUTION

Since the function on the right-hand side is linear, we use the trial function

$$y = lx + m, \text{ which gives } \frac{dy}{dx} = l \text{ and } \frac{d^2y}{dx^2} = 0.$$

Substituting these into the differential equation gives

$$0 + 3l + 2(lx + m) = 4x - 1$$
$$\Rightarrow \qquad 2lx + (3l + 2m) = 4x - 1.$$

Equating coefficients of x, $2l = 4 \Rightarrow l = 2$

Equating the constant terms, $3l + 2m = -1 \Rightarrow m = -\frac{7}{2}$

So a particular integral is $2x - \frac{7}{2}$.

EXAMPLE 6.11

Find a particular integral of the differential equation

$$\frac{d^2x}{dt^2} - 2\frac{dx}{dt} = 3\cos2t.$$

SOLUTION

Since the function on the right-hand side is trigonometric, you use the trial function

The angle used in the trial function is the same angle ($2t$) as appears in the function on the right-hand side of the differential equation.

$$x = l\sin2t + m\cos2t.$$

Although $\sin2t$ does not appear on the right-hand side of the differential equation, you still need to include it in the trial function.

Differentiating this gives

$$\frac{dx}{dt} = 2l\cos2t - 2m\sin2t$$

and

$$\frac{d^2x}{dt^2} = -4l\sin2t - 4m\cos2t.$$

Substituting these into the differential equation gives

$$(-4l\sin2t - 4m\cos2t) - 2(2l\cos2t - 2m\sin2t) \equiv 3\cos2t$$

$$\Rightarrow \qquad (-4l + 4m)\sin2t + (-4l - 4m)\cos2t \equiv 3\cos2t.$$

Equating coefficients of $\sin2t$, $-4l + 4m = 0$

Equating coefficients of $\cos2t$, $-4l - 4m = 3$

Solving for l and m gives $l = -\frac{3}{8}$ and $m = -\frac{3}{8}$.

The particular integral is therefore

$$-\frac{3}{8}\sin2t - \frac{3}{8}\cos2t.$$

Notice that $\sin2t$ appears in the particular integral even though it was not present on the right-hand side of the differential equation.

Sometimes the right-hand side of the differential equation is the sum of different types of function. In such cases your trial function must also be a similar sum, as shown in the next example.

EXAMPLE 6.12

Find a particular integral for the differential equation

$$\frac{d^2h}{dt^2} - \frac{dh}{dt} - 6h = 3t + e^{-t}.$$

SOLUTION

The trial function needs to have two elements:

* to match the $3t$ on the right-hand side it needs to contain $lt + m$
* to match the e^{-t} on the right-hand side it needs to contain ce^{-t}.

The trial function is therefore $h = lt + m + ce^{-t}$.

Differentiating the trial function, you obtain

$$\frac{dh}{dt} = l - ce^{-t}$$

and $\quad \frac{d^2h}{dt^2} = ce^{-t}$.

Substituting these into the differential equation gives

$$ce^{-t} - (l - ce^{-t}) - 6(lt + m + ce^{-t}) \equiv 3t + e^{-t}$$
$$\Rightarrow \qquad -6lt - 1 - 6m - 4ce^{-t} \equiv 3t + e^{-t}.$$

Equating coefficients of t: $-6l = 3 \qquad \Rightarrow \qquad l = -\frac{1}{2}$

Equating constants: $-l - 6m = 0 \qquad \Rightarrow \qquad m = \frac{1}{12}$

Equating coefficients of e^{-t}: $-4c = 1 \qquad \Rightarrow \qquad c = -\frac{1}{4}$.

A particular integral is therefore $-\frac{1}{2}t + \frac{1}{12} - \frac{1}{4}e^{-t}$.

Special cases

In some differential equations the function on the right-hand side has the same form as one of the complementary functions. For example, the complementary function of the differential equation

$$\frac{d^2y}{dx^2} - 5\frac{dy}{dx} + 6y = 4e^{3x}$$

is $Ae^{2x} + Be^{2x}$, and e^{3x} occurs on the right-hand side. In this situation it is no good using the trial function ce^{3x}, since upon substituting $y = ce^{3x}$, $\frac{dy}{dx} = 3ce^{3x}$ and $\frac{d^2y}{dx^2} = 9ce^{3x}$ into the differential equation, you obtain

$$9ce^{3x} - 5(3ce^{3x}) + 6(ce^{3x}) = 4e^{3x}$$
$$\Rightarrow \qquad 0 = 4e^{3x}$$

and so clearly this trial function does not work.

Instead, $y = cxe^{3x}$ is used as a trial function.

This gives $\quad \frac{dy}{dx} = ce^{3x} + 3cxe^{3x}$

and $\quad \frac{d^2y}{dx^2} = 6ce^{3x} + 9cxe^{3x}$.

Substituting these in the differential equation gives

$$(6ce^{3x} + 9cxe^{3x}) - 5(ce^{3x} + 3cxe^{3x}) + 6cxe^{3x} \equiv 4e^{3x}$$
$$\Rightarrow \qquad\qquad ce^{3x} = 4e^{3x}$$
$$\Rightarrow \qquad\qquad c = 4.$$

A particular integral is $4xe^{3x}$.

This illustrates a general rule. If the function on the right-hand side of the differential equation has exactly the same form as one of the complementary functions, you multiply the usual trial function by the independent variable to give a new trial function. In order to recognise these special cases when they arise, it is worth getting into the habit of finding the complementary function before the particular integral.

ACTIVITY

Find the values of c and d that would be obtained if the trial function $ce^x + dxe^x$ were to be used to find a particular integral for the equation

$$\frac{d^2y}{dx^2} - 5\frac{dy}{dx} + 6y = e^x.$$

EXERCISE 6F

Find a particular integral for each of the following differential equations.

1 $\dfrac{d^2y}{dx^2} - 4\dfrac{dy}{dx} + y = -2x + 3$

2 $\dfrac{d^2x}{dt^2} + 4x = t + 2$

3 $4\dfrac{d^2y}{dx^2} - \dfrac{dy}{dx} + 3y = 5x - 1$

4 $\dfrac{d^2x}{dt^2} + \omega^2 x = l$, where ω and l are constants.

5 $\dfrac{d^2v}{dt^2} - 2v = t + 3$

6 $3\dfrac{d^2y}{dx^2} + \dfrac{dy}{dx} = x - 4$

7 $\dfrac{d^2y}{dx^2} + 2\dfrac{dy}{dx} + y = \cos3x$

8 $\dfrac{d^2y}{dx^2} + 2\dfrac{dy}{dx} + y = \sin4x$

9 $\dfrac{dv}{dt} - 3v = 2\sin t$

10 $\dfrac{d^2x}{dt^2} + 9x = 3\cos2t$

11 $\dfrac{d^2x}{dt^2} - 4x = \sin\omega t$

12 $\dfrac{d^2x}{dt^2} + 4\dfrac{dx}{dt} + x = \cos t - 2\sin t$

13 $\dfrac{d^2y}{dx^2} + 4y = e^{-x}$

14 $\dfrac{d^2x}{dt^2} + \dfrac{dx}{dt} + 2x = 3e^{-2t}$

15 $\dfrac{dy}{dx} - 3y = 5e^{2x}$

16 $\dfrac{d^2x}{dt^2} - 5\dfrac{dx}{dt} = 2e^{-3t}$

Finding general and particular solutions

Now that you have seen how to find particular integrals in a variety of situations, you are in a position to find the general solutions of many differential equations. It is then a simple matter to substitute any given conditions into the general solution to find a particular solution. The next example shows how this is done.

EXAMPLE 6.13

Find the particular solution of the differential equation

$$\frac{d^2x}{dt^2} + 9x = 13e^{2t} - 18$$

subject to the conditions $x = 1$ and $\frac{dx}{dt} = 11$ when $t = 0$.

SOLUTION

The auxiliary equation is $\lambda^2 + 9 = 0$

which has roots $\lambda = -3j$ and $\lambda = 3j$.

The complementary function is therefore

$$x = A\sin3t + B\cos3t.$$

To find a particular integral, you use the trial function $x = ce^{2t} + k$.

Differentiating this gives

$$\frac{dx}{dt} = 2ce^{2t}$$

and $\quad \frac{d^2x}{dt^2} = 4ce^{2t}.$

Substituting into the differential equation and simplifying:

$$4ce^{2t} + 9(ce^{2t} + k) \equiv 13e^{2t} - 18$$

Equating coefficients of e^{2t}: $13c = 13 \quad \Rightarrow \quad c = 1$

Equating constants: $9k = -18 \quad\quad \Rightarrow \quad k = -2$

A particular integral is $e^{2t} - 2$.

So the general solution of the differential equation is

$$x = A\sin3t + B\cos3t + e^{2t} - 2.$$

The initial conditions give the values for the unknown constants A and B.

$$x = 1 \text{ when } t = 0 \quad \Rightarrow \quad B + 1 - 2 = 1 \quad \Rightarrow \quad B = 2;$$

$$\frac{dx}{dt} = 11 \text{ when } t = 0$$

$$\Rightarrow \quad 3A\cos3t - 3B\sin3t + 2e^{2t} = 11 \text{ when } t = 0,$$

i.e. $\quad 3A + 2 = 11 \quad \Rightarrow \quad A = 3.$

The particular solution is

$$x = \sin3t + 2\cos3t + e^{2t} - 2.$$

Historical note

The solution of second and higher order differential equations with constant coefficients was first undertaken by Euler. The treatment of the special case when the auxiliary equation has equal roots is due to d'Alembert.

Jean-le-Rond d'Alembert was born in Paris in 1717. He was abandoned at birth and found by a policeman near the church of Saint Jean-le-Rond, whence his name. As an adult, working at the French Academy he pioneered the development of partial differential equations.

EXERCISE 6G

1 Find the general solutions of the following differential equations.

(i) $\dfrac{d^2y}{dx^2} + 4y = e^x + e^{2x}$

(ii) $\dfrac{d^2x}{dt^2} - 2\dfrac{dx}{dt} - 3x = 5e^{-2t} + 10e^{4t}$

(iii) $\dfrac{d^2y}{dx^2} + 2y = 3e^x + \sin x$

(iv) $\dfrac{d^2y}{dx^2} + \dfrac{dy}{dx} + y = \cos x + 4$

(v) $\dfrac{d^2y}{dx^2} + \dfrac{dy}{dx} + y = 3x + 2 + e^x$

(vi) $\dfrac{d^2y}{dx^2} + y = \sin x$

(vii) $\dfrac{d^2y}{dx^2} + 3\dfrac{dy}{dx} - 4y = e^x$

(viii) $\dfrac{d^2y}{dx^2} - 4\dfrac{dy}{dx} + 3y = 2e^x + e^{3x}$

(ix) $\dfrac{d^2y}{dx^2} - 6\dfrac{dy}{dx} + 9y = 4e^{3x}$

(x) $\dfrac{d^2y}{dx^2} - 2\dfrac{dy}{dx} = x$

2 Find the particular solution of each of the following differential equations with the given initial conditions.

(i) $\dfrac{d^2y}{dx^2} - 5\dfrac{dy}{dx} + 6y = 36x$; $y = 0$ and $\dfrac{dy}{dx} = -10$ when $x = 0$.

(ii) $\dfrac{d^2y}{dt^2} + 9x = 20e^{-t}$; $x = 0$ and $\dfrac{dy}{dt} = 1$ when $t = 0$.

(iii) $\dfrac{d^2y}{dx^2} + 2\dfrac{dy}{dx} + 5y = 4e^{-x}$; $y = 0$ and $\dfrac{dy}{dx} = 0$ when $x = 0$.

(iv) $\dfrac{d^2x}{dt^2} + \dfrac{dx}{dt} - 2x = 20\sin 2t$; $x = 2$ and $\dfrac{dx}{dt} = 0$ when $t = 0$.

(v) $\dfrac{d^2y}{dx^2} + \dfrac{dy}{dx} = x$, $y = 1$ and $\dfrac{dy}{dx} = 0$ when $x = 0$.

(vi) $\dfrac{d^2x}{dt^2} - 3\dfrac{dx}{dt} + 2x = 1 - e^t$; $x = 0$ and $\dfrac{dx}{dt} = 1$ when $t = 0$.

(vii) $\dfrac{d^2y}{dx^2} + 4y = 12\sin 2x$; $y = 0$ and $\dfrac{dy}{dx} = 1$ when $x = 0$.

(viii) $\dfrac{d^2y}{dx^2} + 4\dfrac{dy}{dx} + 5y = 8\sin x$; $y = 1$ and $\dfrac{dy}{dx} = 0$ when $x = 0$.

(ix) $\dfrac{d^2y}{dx^2} + 4\dfrac{dy}{dx} + 4y = 8e^{2x} + 4x$; $y = 0$ and $\dfrac{dy}{dx} = 1$ when $x = 0$.

(x) $\dfrac{d^2y}{dx^2} + 4\dfrac{dy}{dx} + 4y = e^{-2x}$; $y = 0.5$ and $\dfrac{dy}{dx} = 0$ when $x = 0$.

3 A biological population of size P at time t is growing in an environment which can support a maximum population which is subject to seasonal variation. The growth of the population is described by the first order linear differential equation

$$\frac{dP}{dt} + P = 100 + 50\sin t.$$

Find

(i) the complementary function of this differential equation

(ii) the particular integral

(iii) the complete solution given that initially $P = 20$

(iv) the mean size of the population after a long time has elapsed

(v) the amplitude of the oscillations of the population.

[MEI]

4 The second order linear differential equation

$$y'' + (\tan x)y' = e^{-x}\cos x,$$

$$y(0) = 1, \; y'(0) = \tfrac{1}{2},$$

is to be solved. It may be reduced to a linear first order equation by the substitution $y' = v$.

(i) Write down the first order equation for v.

(ii) Solve this equation to find v as a function of x.

(iii) Hence find y as a function of x.

(iv) Determine the value of y when $x = \tfrac{1}{4}\pi$.

[The result

$$\int e^{-x}\cos x\,dx = \tfrac{1}{2}(\sin x - \cos x)e^{-x}$$

may be assumed.]

[MEI]

5 (i) Find the general solution of the differential equation

$$y'' + 3y' + 2y = 2x + 1.$$

(ii) Find the particular solution for which $y = -1$, $y' = 0$ when $x = 0$.

(iii) Show that $y' = 0$ when $2u^2 - u - 1 = 0$, where $u = e^{-x}$. Deduce that $y' = 0$ only when $x = 0$. Find the value of x for which $y'' = 0$. Hence or otherwise show that $y' \leqslant \tfrac{9}{8}$ for all values of x.

(iv) Hence sketch the graph of y against x.

[MEI]

6 (i) A solution is sought to the differential equation

$$\frac{d^2y}{dx^2} + 2\frac{dy}{dx} + 10y = 18e^{-x}.$$

(a) Find the general solution. You are given that when $x = 0$, $y = 0$ and $\dfrac{dy}{dx} = 0$.

(b) Find the solution subject to these conditions.

(c) Calculate the smallest two positive values of x for which $y = 0$. Sketch the solution, clearly marking these values.

(iii) Find the general solution of the differential equation

$$\frac{d^3y}{dx^3} + 2\frac{d^2y}{dx^2} + 10\frac{dy}{dx} = 0.$$

[MEI]

7 (i) Given that $p(x)$ is a particular integral of the differential equation

$$y'' + by' + cy = f(x)$$

and $q(x)$ is a particular integral of the differential equation

$$y'' + by' + cy = g(x),$$

show that a particular integral of the differential equation

$$y'' + by' + cy = f(x) + g(x)$$

is $p(x) + q(x)$.

(ii) The voltage V in a circuit at time t is modelled by the differential equation

$$\ddot{V} + 2\dot{V} + 5V = t + e^{-t}.$$

(a) Find a complementary function as the sum of two linearly independent functions.

(b) Using the results of part (i) find a particular integral of the differential equation.

(c) Write down a general solution containing two arbitrary constants.

[MEI]

8 A solution is sought to the differential equation

$$\ddot{y} + 4\dot{y} + 4y = 2e^{-2t}.$$

(i) Find the complementary function.

(ii) Explain why an expression of either of the forms ae^{-2t} or ate^{-2t} cannot be a particular integral of the differential equation. State a correct form for the particular integral and hence show that the general solution is

$$y = (A + Bt + t^2)e^{-2t},$$

where A and B are arbitrary constants.

(iii) It is given that $y = 0$ when $t = 1$ and that $y = 0$ when $t = 3$. Calculate the constants A and B and write the particular solution in factorised form.

(iv) By reference to the previous answer, write down the particular solution in the cases
   (a) $y = 0$ when $t = 2$ and $y = 0$ when $t = 7$
   (b) $y = 0$ only when $t = 1$.

Write down an example of a particular solution which is never zero. Justify your answer.

[MEI]

9 A solution is sought to the differential equation

$$\ddot{y} + 3\dot{y} + 2y = e^{kt}\sin t,$$

where k is a constant.

(i) In the case $k = 0$, find the general solution.

Find also the particular solution for which $y = \dot{y} = 0$ when $t = 0$.

(ii) In the case $k = 1$, verify that $y = \frac{1}{10}e^t(\sin t - \cos t)$ is a particular integral for the differential equation. Write down the general solution.

(iii) Compare the behaviour of the solutions in the two cases $k = 0$ and $k = 1$ for large values of t.

In the case $k = -1$, what would you expect the behaviour of the solution to be for large values of t?

[MEI]

10 The current, I amperes, in an electrical circuit at time t seconds after being switched on is modelled by the differential equation

$$\frac{d^2I}{dt^2} + 4\frac{dI}{dt} + 4I = -5\sin t.$$

(i) Find the general solution.

Initially there is no current flowing but $\frac{dI}{dt} = 5$.

(ii) Show that the solution is

$$I = \frac{4}{5}\cos t - \frac{3}{5}\sin t + \left(4t - \frac{4}{5}\right)e^{-2t}.$$

The exponentially decaying terms of the solution form the transient current. The non-decaying term forms the steady state current.

(iii) Calculate the amplitude of the steady state current. Express the steady state current in the form $R\cos t(t + \alpha)$, calculating α correct to 4 significant figures.

(iv) Calculate the maximum value of the transient current. What is the value of I at this time?

[MEI]

11 The current in an electrical circuit consisting of an inductor, resistor and capacitor in series with an exponentially decaying power source is modelled by the equation

$$10\frac{d^2I}{dt^2} + 2k\frac{dI}{dt} + I = 18e^{-\frac{1}{10}t},$$

where I is the current in amperes and t is the time in seconds after the power source is switched on. The value of the positive constant k can be adjusted by varying the resistance.

In the case $k = 1$,

(i) find the general solution

(ii) find the particular solution for which

$$\frac{dI}{dt} = I = 0 \text{ when } t = 0.$$

The resistance is adjusted so that the current will not oscillate.

(iii) Show that the minimum value of k required to achieve this is $\sqrt{10}$.

With $k = \sqrt{10}$ and the power source removed, the equation modelling the current is

$$10\frac{d^2I}{dt^2} + 2\sqrt{10}\frac{dI}{dt} + I = 0,$$

with $I = 4$ and $\frac{dI}{dt} = a$ when $t = 0$.

(iv) Find the general solution of this equation. Determine the range of values of α for which the current will not be zero at any finite time.

[MEI]

12 A solution is sought to the differential equation

$$\frac{dy}{dx} + 2y = e^{-2t}.$$

(i) Find the complementary function.

(ii) Explain why an expression of the form ae^{-2t} cannot be a particular integral of this differential equation. Find a particular integral of this differential equation.

An alternative method for solving this equation is by using an integrating factor.

(iii) Use this method to find the general solution of the differential equation. Hence show that the particular integral found in part (ii) is correct.

(iv) When $t = 0$, $y = y_0$. Show that the maximum value of y is $\frac{1}{2}e^{2y_0-1}$. State the range of values of y_0 for which this maximum occurs at a positive value of t.

[MEI]

13 Three differential equations are being studied for $x > 0$. The first is

$$\frac{dy}{dx} + \frac{y}{x} = e^x. \qquad \text{①}$$

(i) Use the integrating factor method to find the general solution of equation ①.

(ii) Given that $y = 1$ when $x = 1$, show that the particular solution is $y = \frac{(x-1)e^x + 1}{x}$.

Use the approximation $e^x \approx 1 + x$, for small x, to describe the behaviour of y as x tends to zero.

Sketch a graph of the solution.

The other two differential equations are

$$\frac{dy}{dx} + y = e^x, \qquad \text{②}$$

$$\frac{dy}{dx} + ye^x = e^x. \qquad \text{③}$$

(iii) Use a method other than the integrating factor method to find the general solution of equation ②

(iv) Equation ③ can be solved by a different method from equations ① and ②. Use this method to find the general solution of equation ③.

[MEI]

14 A solution is sought to the differential equation

$$\frac{d^2y}{dx^2} + \frac{dy}{dx} + ky = 12e^{-x},$$

where k is a constant.

Consider the case $k = -2$.

(i) Find the general solution.

You are given that y tends to zero as x tends to infinity and that $\frac{dy}{dx} = 2$ when $x = 0$.

(ii) Find the particular solution.

(iii) Find the finite value of x for which y is zero.

Consider now the case $k = \frac{1}{4}$. You are again given that y tends to zero as x tends to infinity and that $\frac{dy}{dx} = 2$ when $x = 0$.

(iv) Show that, in this case, the given conditions are not sufficient to determine the particular solution.

[MEI]

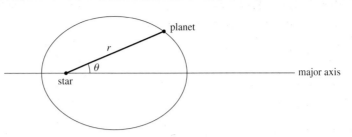

Figure 6.7

Figure 6.7 shows a planet of mass m in an elliptical orbit round a star of mass M. The distance of the planet from the star at time t is r and its displacement vector from the star makes an angle θ with the major axis of the ellipse.

The general orbit under the inverse square law of gravitation is described by the differential equation

$$\frac{d^2u}{d\theta^2} + u = \frac{GM}{h^2}$$

where $u = \dfrac{1}{r}$, G is the universal constant of gravitation, and h is a constant $\left(h \text{ is actually the angular momentum of the planet given by } mr^2\dfrac{d\theta}{dt} \right)$.

Solve this differential equation and investigate the possible solutions. What condition must be satisfied for u to take the value zero? What does this then mean about the nature of the orbit?

KEY POINTS

1 A second order linear differential equation with constant coefficients can be written in the form

$$\frac{d^2y}{dx^2} + a\frac{dy}{dx} + by = f(x),$$

where a and b are constants.

2 The equation is homogeneous if $f(x) = 0$. Otherwise it is non-homogenous.

3 When you are given a differential equation of the form above, you can immediately write down the auxiliary equation

$$\lambda^2 + a\lambda + b = 0.$$

4 Each root of the auxiliary equation determines the form of one of the complementary functions.

5 If the auxiliary equation has two real, distinct roots λ_1 and λ_2 then the complementary function of the differential equation is

$$y = Ae^{\lambda_1 x} + Be^{\lambda_2 x}.$$

6 If the auxiliary equation has complex roots $\lambda = \alpha + \beta j$ and $\lambda = \alpha - \beta j$, then the complementary function of the differential equation is

$$y = e^{\alpha x}(A\sin\beta x + B\cos\beta x).$$

7 If the auxiliary equation has a repeated root $\lambda = \alpha$ then the complementary function of the differential equation is

$$y = e^{\alpha x}(A + Bx) = Ae^{\alpha x} + Bxe^{\alpha x}.$$

8 The general solution of the non-homogeneous linear differential equation with constant coefficients

$$\frac{d^2 y}{dx^2} + a\frac{dy}{dx} + by = f(x)$$

is the sum of the complementary function and a particular integral.

9 The number of unknown constants is the same as the order of the equation.

10 A particular integral is any function that satisfies the full equation; it does not contain any arbitrary constants.

11 To find the particular integral, use the trial function shown in the following table.

Function	Trial function
linear function	$lx + m$
polynominal of order n	$a_n x^n + a_{n-1} x^{n-1} + \ldots + a_1 x + a_0$
trigonometric function involving $\sin px$ and $\cos px$	$l\sin px + m\cos px$
exponential function involving e^{px}	ce^{px}

12 If the trial function for a particular integral is the same as one of the complementary functions, you multiply the trial function by x.

7 Oscillations

Human nature oscillates between good and evil.

Jowett

❓ The photographs show three situations in which bodies or particles oscillate. List the similarities between the motion of the bodies (or particles) in these situations.

In the next two chapters you will see how the use of differential equations allows you to develop mathematical models which give a very good description of such situations.

When listing the similarities between different oscillating motions you may have come up with the following.

- The motion follows a regular cyclic (repeating) pattern.
- The body (or particles) move backwards and forwards through a central position.
- The two extreme points of the motion are at equal distances from the central point.
- The velocity of the body (or particles) is greatest at the central position.
- The velocity is instantaneously zero at each extreme of the motion.

These are all true. In fact, remarkably, if you plot the displacement of almost any oscillating body or particle against time, you will find it to be a sine curve.

Notation

Before you can write down any equations you need suitable notation and terminology.

- The central position is usually called O.
- The two extreme points of motion have displacements $\pm a$ from O. The distance a is called the *amplitude* of the motion.
- The number of cycles per second is called the *frequency* of the oscillation, and is usually denoted by v (the Greek letter 'nu').
- The motion repeats itself after time T. The time interval T is called the *period*: it is the time for one cycle of the motion. Notice that T and v are connected: if the time for one cycle is $\frac{1}{2}$ second, then the frequency is 2 cycles per second. In general

$$T = \frac{1}{v}.$$

The SI unit for frequency is the *hertz*. One hertz (1 Hz) is one cycle per second.

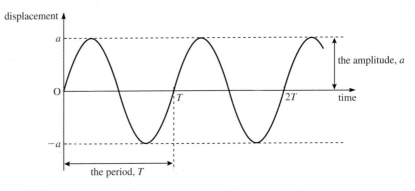

Figure 7.1

Modelling oscillating systems

The first step is to set up mathematical models for the motion of two simple systems, the spring–mass oscillator and the simple pendulum. In each case you will see that applying Newton's second law gives rise to a second order differential equation.

The spring–mass oscillator

The spring–mass oscillator consists of an elastic spring attached to a fixed point and at the other end is attached an object. The system is hung vertically as shown in figure 7.2. If the object is displaced vertically from the equilibrium position and then released, the object oscillates along a straight vertical line.

Figure 7.2

Before you can analyse this motion you need to make some modelling assumptions:

- the effects of friction in the spring and air resistance on the object may be neglected
- the spring is light and perfectly elastic: this means that the tension in the spring is proportional to its extension.

The constant of proportionality between the tension and the extension of the spring is called its *stiffness*, and is denoted by k. The natural length of the spring is l_0, and the mass of the object is m. You can find the extension, e, of the spring when the object is in equilibrium by looking at the forces acting on the object in equilibrium (figure 7.3).

There is a downward force mg due to gravity, and a balancing upward tension in the spring. The tension is given by $T = ke$. Since the system is in equilibrium

$$ke = mg$$
$$\Rightarrow \quad e = \frac{mg}{k}.$$

Figure 7.3

Now look at the system when the spring has a further extension x below the equilibrium position, so that the total extension is $e + x$ (figure 7.4). The tension T in the spring is now $T = k(e + x)$.

The object is not in equilibrium, and its acceleration in the downward direction (the direction of increasing x) is

$$\frac{\mathrm{d}^2x}{\mathrm{d}t^2}.$$

Applying Newton's second law gives the differential equation

$$m\frac{\mathrm{d}^2x}{\mathrm{d}t^2} = mg - T$$
$$= mg - k(e + x)$$
$$= mg - ke - kx.$$

Figure 7.4

But you have already seen that $mg - ke = 0$.

Substituting this in the differential equation and dividing by m gives the equation of motion

$$\frac{\mathrm{d}^2x}{\mathrm{d}t^2} + \frac{k}{m}x = 0 \quad \text{or} \quad \frac{\mathrm{d}^2x}{\mathrm{d}t^2} = -\frac{k}{m}x.$$

This differential equation models the motion of the idealised spring–mass oscillator.

The simple pendulum

A pendulum consists of a small heavy object, the *bob*, suspended from a fixed point by a string. If the bob is displaced by a small angle from its equilibrium position, then it will swing back and forth. Its path will be an arc of a circle.

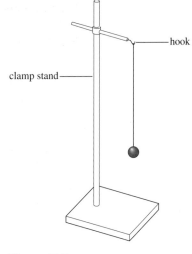

As with the spring–mass oscillator, you need to start with some modelling assumptions:

- the bob can be treated as a particle
- the string is light
- the string is inelastic (and therefore has constant length)

Figure 7.5

- the oscillations are small enough for the maximum angle between the string and the vertical to satisfy the approximation $\sin\theta \approx \theta$. (This is accurate to 2 decimal places if the angle is no more than 0.3 radians or 17°.)

This idealised system is called a *simple pendulum*.

Let the mass of the bob be m and the length of the string be l. The bob then swings through a small arc of a circle of radius l. At time t let the angle of the string with the vertical be θ in radians.

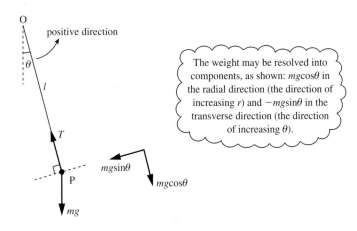

The weight may be resolved into components, as shown: $mg\cos\theta$ in the radial direction (the direction of increasing r) and $-mg\sin\theta$ in the transverse direction (the direction of increasing θ).

Figure 7.6

Figure 7.6 shows the forces on the object, the weight mg of the bob and the tension T in the string.

The acceleration in the transverse direction is given by $l\dfrac{d^2\theta}{dt^2}$.

Applying Newton's second law in the transverse direction gives

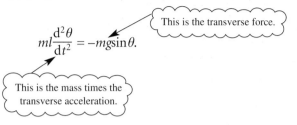

$$ml\dfrac{d^2\theta}{dt^2} = -mg\sin\theta.$$

This is the transverse force.

This is the mass times the transverse acceleration.

Dividing both sides by m and using the small angle approximation $\sin\theta \approx \theta$, the equation of motion is

$$l\dfrac{d^2\theta}{dt^2} + g\theta = 0.$$

This can alternatively be written as

$$\dfrac{d^2\theta}{dt^2} + \dfrac{g}{l}\theta = 0 \quad \text{or} \quad \dfrac{d^2\theta}{dt^2} = -\dfrac{g}{l}\theta.$$

This equation models the motion of a simple pendulum.

Simple harmonic motion

Look at the differential equations that arose from the two previous examples and you will see something that is both remarkable and exciting. They both have the same form:

$$\dfrac{d^2x}{dt^2} = -\omega^2 x.$$

In the first case $\omega^2 = \dfrac{k}{m}$, in the second $\omega^2 = \dfrac{g}{l}$. In the second example the variable is called θ rather than x.

The fact that the spring–mass oscillator and the simple pendulum give rise to essentially the same equation of motion shows that the motion is, in both cases, fundamentally the same. This motion is called *simple harmonic motion* (SHM); it provides a model for many oscillations.

Solving the simple harmonic motion equation

You can use the auxiliary equation method to solve the equation of simple harmonic motion, and this is done below.

The auxiliary equation is

$$\lambda^2 + \omega^2 = 0$$

which has roots $\lambda = \pm j\omega$.

The general solution of the differential equation is then

$$y = A\sin\omega t + B\cos\omega t.$$

The constants of integration, A and B, are unknown at this stage, but if you know suitable initial or boundary conditions you can calculate their values.

ACTIVITY

Find the particular solution of the SHM equation given the conditions $x = 0$ when $t = 0$, $x = a$ when $t = \dfrac{\pi}{2\omega}$. Sketch a graph of x against t for this situation.

You should have found that in this case the particular solution was the simple sine expression, $x = a\sin\omega t$, because B turned out to have the value zero. But what happens when the initial conditions are not so convenient?

If the general solution for the motion has the form of a sine curve it should be possible to write $A\sin\omega t + B\cos\omega t$ in the form $a\sin(\omega t + \varepsilon)$, where a is the amplitude of the motion and ε (the Greek letter 'epsilon') is a constant angle. This still contains two unknown constants, but it is more immediately recognisable as a sine function.

To show that this is indeed possible we write

$$A\sin\omega t + B\cos\omega t \equiv a\sin(\omega t + \varepsilon)$$

and expand the right-hand side using the compound-angle formula. This gives

$$A\sin\omega t + B\cos\omega t \equiv a\sin\omega t \cos\varepsilon + a\cos\omega t \sin\varepsilon.$$

Comparing coefficients of $\sin\omega t$: $A = a\cos\varepsilon$ ①
Comparing coefficients of $\cos\omega t$: $B = a\sin\varepsilon$.   ②

Squaring ① and ② and adding them gives

$$A^2 + B^2 = a^2(\cos^2\varepsilon + \sin^2\varepsilon) = a^2$$
$$\Rightarrow \qquad a = \sqrt{A^2 + B^2}.$$

Dividing ② by ① gives

$$\tan\varepsilon = \frac{B}{A}.$$

So the general solution of the simple harmonic motion equation can indeed be expressed as a sine function. This tells us a lot about the solution.

- Since the sine function varies between $+1$ and -1, the solution varies between $+a$ and $-a$.
- Since the sine function is periodic with period 2π, the solution is periodic with period $\dfrac{2\pi}{\omega}$.
- The velocity and acceleration of the motion, found by differentiating the solution with respect to t, are given respectively by $a\omega\cos(\omega t + \varepsilon)$ and $-a\omega^2\sin(\omega t + \varepsilon)$.

ACTIVITY

Given that $x = a\sin(\omega t + \varepsilon)$, sketch the graph of x against t for the following values of ε.

(i) $\varepsilon = 0$ **(ii)** $\varepsilon = \dfrac{\pi}{4}$ **(iii)** $\varepsilon = \dfrac{\pi}{2}$

What is the frequency of the oscillations in each case, in terms of ω?

What is the effect of the constant ε?

You should have found in the activity above that in each case the frequency is $\dfrac{\omega}{2\pi}$, and is unaffected by ε. The frequency therefore depends only on ω, which is a constant for a given pendulum, or for a particular spring–mass combination. Notice that ω is not itself the frequency, v; that is given by $v = \dfrac{\omega}{2\pi}$. (The term *angular frequency* is sometimes used to describe ω.)

The effect of ε is simply to shift the sine curve to the left by an amount $\dfrac{\varepsilon}{\omega}$, as shown in figure 7.7.

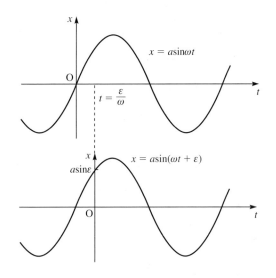

Figure 7.7

Changing the magnitude of ε does not affect the frequency of the oscillation or its amplitude. Its effect is just to position the curve correctly relative to the time axis, depending on the point in the cycle at which the time is taken to be zero. The quantity ε is called the *phase shift*.

ACTIVITY

You may sometimes find it more convenient to write the general solution in another equivalent form:

$$y = a\cos(\omega t + \varepsilon_1)$$

Find a and ε_1 in terms of A and B in this case.

EXAMPLE 7.1

A spring–mass oscillator consists of a spring of stiffness 20 Nm^{-1} and natural length 0.5 m and an object of mass 0.25 kg. The oscillator lies on a smooth horizontal table with one end of the spring attached to a fixed point (as in figure 7.8). The object is constrained to move along a smooth groove.

Figure 7.8

The object is pulled to the right so that the spring is 0.6 m in length, and the object is released from rest at this point when $t = 0$.

(i) Form the differential equation for the system and write down the initial conditions.

(ii) Find the particular solution describing the motion.

(iii) Write down the period and amplitude of the motion.

(iv) Sketch a graph of the solution.

SOLUTION

(i) You assume that the spring is perfectly elastic and has zero mass, and that the effects of friction and air resistance may be neglected. The object is in equilibrium when the spring has its natural length. At time t (in seconds), let the extension of the spring be x metres. (At this point the object is a distance x to the right of its equilibrium position, see figure 7.9.)

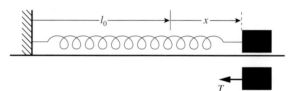

Figure 7.9

The acceleration of the object at time t is $\dfrac{d^2x}{dt^2}$ in the positive horizontal direction. The only horizontal force is the tension, T newtons, in the spring. The tension is given by

$$T = kx = 20x.$$

Applying Newton's second law $F = ma$ gives

This is the force; it has a negative sign because the tension acts in the negative direction.

$$-20x = 0.25\frac{d^2x}{dt^2}$$

This is the acceleration, a.

This is the mass, m.

$$\Rightarrow \quad \frac{d^2x}{dt^2} + 80x = 0.$$

This is the differential equation of motion of the system.

Initially the object is at rest, so $\dfrac{dx}{dt} = 0$ when $t = 0$. The extension of the spring is initially 0.1 m, so $x = 0.1$ when $t = 0$. These are the initial conditions.

(ii) The equation of motion is

$$\frac{d^2x}{dt^2} + 80x = 0,$$

which is of the form

$$\frac{d^2x}{dt^2} = -\omega^2 x$$

for which $x = A\sin\omega t + B\cos\omega t$ where $\omega = \sqrt{80}$.

Substituting the initial conditions into the general solution:

When $t = 0$, $x = 0.1$ $\quad\Rightarrow\quad$ $0.1 = B$.

When $t = 0$, $\dfrac{dx}{dt} = 0$ $\quad\Rightarrow\quad$ $0 = A\omega$, and so $A = 0$.

The particular solution is

$$x = 0.1\cos\sqrt{80}\,t.$$

(iii) The amplitude of the motion is 0.1 m and the period is

$$\frac{2\pi}{\omega} = \frac{2\pi}{\sqrt{80}} \approx 0.7 \text{ seconds.}$$

(iv) The graph of displacement x against time t is as shown in figure 7.10.

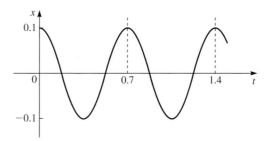

Figure 7.10

Starting with the general solution of the SHM equation, $x = a\sin(\omega t + \varepsilon)$, show that when the displacement is x, the velocity and acceleration are given by

$$v = \pm\omega\sqrt{a^2 - x^2} \text{ and } a = -\omega^2 x.$$

7

1 A spring–mass oscillator consists of a spring of stiffness $32\,\mathrm{Nm^{-1}}$, natural length $0.5\,\mathrm{m}$ and an object of mass $0.5\,\mathrm{kg}$. The oscillator lies on a smooth horizontal table with one end of the spring attached to a fixed point. The object is constrained to move in a straight line, and friction can be taken to be negligible.

Initially the object is at rest, and the spring is $0.6\,\mathrm{m}$ in length.

  (i) Formulate the differential equation for the system and write down the initial conditions in this case.

  (ii) Find the particular solution describing the motion.

  (iii) Write down the period and amplitude of the motion.

  (iv) Sketch a graph of the solution.

2 A spring–mass oscillator consists of a spring of natural length $0.2\,\mathrm{m}$ and stiffness $25\,\mathrm{Nm^{-1}}$ and an object of mass $0.4\,\mathrm{kg}$. One end of the spring is attached to a fixed point and the system hangs vertically.

  (i) Find the length of the spring when the system is in equilibrium.

The object is pulled down $10\,\mathrm{cm}$ from its equilibrium position and released.

  (ii) Formulate the differential equation for the system and write down the initial conditions in this case.

  (iii) Find the particular solution describing the motion.

  (iv) Write down the period and amplitude of the motion.

  (v) Describe the motion of the object.

3 An object of mass $200\,\mathrm{g}$ is attached to a light spring of natural length $40\,\mathrm{cm}$ and stiffness $50\,\mathrm{Nm^{-1}}$. The object is allowed to hang vertically in equilibrium.

  (i) Find the extension of the spring in this position.

The spring is now pulled down by a further $3\,\mathrm{cm}$ and released from rest.

  (ii) Find the length of the spring as a function of time.

4 Two springs have the same natural length l but have stiffnesses $75\,\mathrm{Nm^{-1}}$ and $50\,\mathrm{Nm^{-1}}$. An object of mass $0.5\,\mathrm{kg}$ is attached to both springs and their other ends are attached to two points which are a distance $d\,\mathrm{m}$ apart on a smooth horizontal table (where $d > 2l$). Find the period of small oscillations of this system.

$k_1 = 75\,\mathrm{Nm^{-1}}$ $0.5\,\mathrm{kg}$ $k_2 = 50\,\mathrm{Nm^{-1}}$

5 A simple pendulum of length $3\,\mathrm{m}$ has a bob of mass $0.2\,\mathrm{kg}$. It is hanging vertically when it is set in motion by a single, sharp sideways blow to the bob which causes the pendulum to oscillate with an angular amplitude of $5°$.

  (i) State the amplitude in radians.

  (ii) Calculate the approximate period of the pendulum.

  (iii) The motion of the pendulum can be modelled by the equation

$$\theta = a\sin(\omega t + \varepsilon).$$

Write down the values of a, ω and ε.

  (iv) Calculate the maximum speed of the pendulum bob according to this model.

6 A pendulum has a bob of mass $0.25\,\mathrm{kg}$. The period of the pendulum is 2 seconds. The amplitude of its swing is $3°$.

  (i) Find the length of the pendulum.

  (ii) State the effect (if any) on the period of the pendulum of:

    (a) making the mass of the bob $0.75\,\mathrm{kg}$

    (b) doubling the length of the pendulum

    (c) halving the amplitude of its swing

    (d) moving it to the moon where the acceleration due to gravity is $\frac{1}{6}g$.

7 A pendulum consists of a bob of mass 0.2 kg attached to a light inelastic string of length 4 m.

(i) Formulate the equation of motion of the bob, stating any assumptions involved.

(ii) Calculate the period of small oscillations.

8 A loaded test tube of total mass m floats in water and is in equilibrium when a length l is submerged as shown. The upward force exerted at any instant by the water on the tube is F.

(i) Why is F equal to mg in the equilibrium position? Given that F is directly proportional to the submerged length, find the constant of proportionality in terms of l, m and g.

The test tube is now pushed down a small amount and released.

(ii) Find F when the bottom of the tube is a distance x below its equilibrium position, and use Newton's second law to write down the equation of motion.

(iii) Find the period of the motion.

9 A particle of mass 0.02 kg is performing simple harmonic motion with centre O, period 6 s and amplitude 2 m. Find, correct to 2 significant figures,

(i) the maximum speed V of the particle

(ii) the distance of the particle from O when its speed is $0.9 V$

(iii) the magnitude of the force acting on the particle when it is 1 m from O.

INVESTIGATION

A *seconds pendulum* is one that swings through its complete arc in 1 second, so that it has a period of 2 seconds.

Set up a seconds pendulum experimentally. What is the length of the pendulum?

Is this what you would have predicted from your knowledge of the SHM model?

Improving the model

Simple harmonic motion has constant amplitude and goes on for ever. For many real oscillating systems, SHM is not a very good model: usually the amplitude of the oscillations gradually decreases, and the motion dies away.

When you find that a model is unsatisfactory, you need to look again at your assumptions. In this case, the assumption that you need to question is that the effects of air resistance and friction can be neglected. Real oscillating systems are almost always *damped*: that is they are affected to some degree by the resistive forces of friction and/or air resistance. They perform *damped oscillations*.

In many systems the damping force is proportional to the speed of the object. This is often represented on a diagram by a device called a linear dashpot, as shown in figure 7.11.

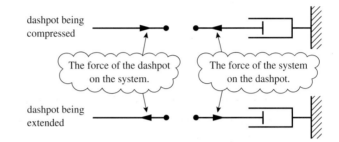

Figure 7.11

A dashpot exerts a force on the system which is proportional to the rate at which it is being extended or compressed, and which acts in the direction opposite to that of the motion. This is illustrated in figure 7.12.

dashpot being compressed → The force of the dashpot on the system. → The force of the system on the dashpot.

dashpot being extended

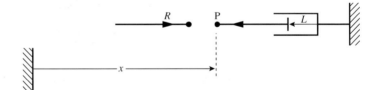

Figure 7.12

The force R that the dashpot exerts on the system at time t is given by

$$R = r\frac{dL}{dt}$$

where the constant of proportionality r is called the *dashpot constant* (or the *damping constant*). The amount of travel still left in the dashpot (see figure 7.13) is denoted by L.

Figure 7.13

It is important to be clear in your mind about the direction of the force R and the signs involved. Look at the point P on the moving part of the dashpot.

- When P is moving from right to left, L is increasing; $\dfrac{dL}{dt}$ is positive and the force is in the same direction as that marked for R in figure 7.13. The dashpot is opposing the right to left motion.
- When P is moving from left to right, L is decreasing, $\dfrac{dL}{dt}$ is negative and the force is in the opposite direction to that marked for R in figure 7.13. The dashpot is now opposing the left to right motion.

Thus the sign of the dashpot force looks after itself as the motion changes.

However you will not usually be interested in the quantity L so much as the distance of the point P from some fixed point of the system. This distance is shown as x in figure 7.13. All the systems that you will meet in this book are set up so that as x increases, L decreases, and vice versa, so

$$\frac{dx}{dt} = -\frac{dL}{dt}.$$

Consequently the force that the dashpot exerts on the system is given by

$$R = -r\frac{dx}{dt}$$

in the direction of increasing x.

Note

Here we are using a dashpot as a symbol to represent damping effects but a dashpot is actually a real device that is often used in man-made systems. It is used when a certain (predictable) amount of damping, over and above that provided by friction and air resistance, is desired. For example, a car's shock-absorber includes a linear dashpot, as shown in the photograph.

Such a dashpot consists of a cylinder containing a viscous liquid, often oil. When the cylinder is compressed or extended a disc moves along the cylinder, and is opposed by a force which is proportional to the speed of compression or extension. The constant of proportionality depends on the viscosity of the liquid.

EXAMPLE 7.2

A simple oscillating system is being modelled as a damped spring–mass oscillator, in which an object of mass 2 kg is attached to fixed points by a spring of natural length 0.5 m, stiffness 20 Nm^{-1} and by a dashpot of constant 12 Nm^{-1} s. The spring–mass–dashpot system lies on a smooth horizontal surface, as shown in the figure 7.14.

Figure 7.14

(i) Formulate the differential equation of motion for this system.

The system is released from rest when the spring length is 0.6 m.

(ii) Find the particular solution of the differential equation that models this situation.

SOLUTION

(i) Figure 7.15 shows the spring–mass–dashpot system at some general time t (seconds), when the extension of the spring is x. The horizontal forces are the tension in the spring, T, and the damping force R.

Figure 7.15

The tension in the spring is $T = kx = 20x$.

The dashpot force is $R = -r\dfrac{dx}{dt} = -12\dfrac{dx}{dt}$.

Applying Newton's second law $F = ma$ at any instant gives

This side is *ma*. $2\dfrac{d^2x}{dt^2} = -12\dfrac{dx}{dt} - 20x$ This side is F where $F = R - T$.

Dividing both sides by 2, and rearranging, you obtain the equation of motion of the spring–mass–dashpot system:

$$\frac{d^2x}{dt^2} + 6\frac{dx}{dt} + 10x = 0.$$

Notice that you again have a linear homogeneous second order equation with constant coefficients.

(ii) The auxiliary equation for the differential equation is

$$\lambda^2 + 6\lambda + 10 = 0$$

$$\Rightarrow \quad \lambda = \frac{-6 \pm \sqrt{6^2 - 40}}{2} = -3 \pm j.$$

The general solution of the differential equation is $x = ae^{-3t}\sin(t + \varepsilon)$.

At the start of the motion, the length of the spring is 0.6 m and the object is at rest, so the initial conditions are $x = 0.1$ and $\dfrac{dx}{dt} = 0$ when $t = 0$.

When $t = 0$, $x = 0.1$ $\quad \Rightarrow \quad a\sin\varepsilon = 0.1$. ①

By differentiating the general solution you obtain

$$\frac{dx}{dt} = -3e^{-3t}\, a\sin(t + \varepsilon) + ae^{-3t}\cos(t + \varepsilon).$$

When $t = 0$, $\dfrac{dx}{dt} = 0$ $\quad \Rightarrow \quad 0 = -3a\sin\varepsilon + a\cos\varepsilon$

$$\Rightarrow \quad \tan\varepsilon = \tfrac{1}{3}.$$

From ① we see that $\sin\varepsilon = \dfrac{0.1}{a}$, which is positive, and so ε must be an angle in the first quadrant.

$$\Rightarrow \quad \varepsilon = 0.322 \text{ (radians) and } a = \frac{0.1}{\sin 0.322} = 0.316.$$

The particular solution in this case is

$$x = 0.316e^{-3t}\sin(t + 0.322).$$

The initial amplitude of the motion is 0.316 m (to 3 decimal places) and the period in seconds is $\dfrac{2\pi}{1} = 2\pi$.

The amplitude decays exponentially. In this case the oscillation decays very quickly.

Figure 7.16 shows the graph of a typical damped oscillation. There are many real situations where the oscillations decrease gradually in amplitude like this. Oscillations of this type are often called *lightly damped* or *underdamped*.

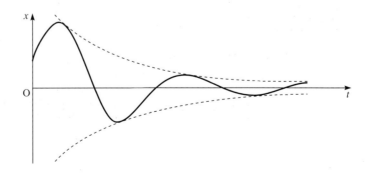

Figure 7.16

The general equation for damped oscillations

The differential equation of motion in the spring–mass–dashpot system above is an example of the general differential equation of a linearly damped system:

$$\frac{d^2y}{dt^2} + a\frac{dy}{dt} + \omega^2 y = 0,$$

where a and ω are positive constants. For a spring–mass–dashpot system, $a = \frac{r}{m}$ where r is the dashpot constant, and $\omega = \sqrt{\frac{k}{m}}$ where k is the stiffness of the spring. The quantity $\frac{\omega}{2\pi}$ is called the *natural frequency* of the system: it is the same whether the system is damped or undamped.

The solution of this differential equation can give several different types of motion, depending on the relative sizes of the parameters a and ω. The auxiliary equation is

$$\lambda^2 + a\lambda + \omega^2 = 0.$$

This has two solutions,

$$\lambda_1 = \frac{-a + \sqrt{a^2 - 4\omega^2}}{2} \quad \text{and} \quad \lambda_2 = \frac{-a - \sqrt{a^2 - 4\omega^2}}{2}.$$

The *discriminant*, $a^2 - 4\omega^2$, determines the nature of the solution. There are three possibilities, as follows.

- *Overdamping*: $a^2 - 4\omega^2$, is positive, and the system does not oscillate (figure 7.17).

Figure 7.17

- *Underdamping*: $a^2 - 4\omega^2$ is negative, and oscillations occur (figure 7.18).

Figure 7.18

- *Critical damping*: $\alpha^2 - 4\omega^2 = 0$ (figure 7.19).

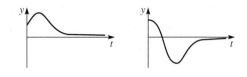

Figure 7.19

Critical damping is the borderline between overdamping and underdamping. It is not obvious in a physical situation when damping is critical, since the pattern of motion for critical damping can be very similar to that in the overdamped case.

 In many systems damping is desirable or even necessary. For each of the following systems, decide whether damping is desirable and if so whether overdamping, underdamping or critical damping is preferable.

(i) A clock pendulum   **(ii)** A car suspension system

(iii) A set of kitchen scales   **(iv)** A robotic welding arm.

EXPERIMENT

Set up a spring–mass–dashpot system as shown in figure 7.20.

Displace the object through a small distance then release it. Describe the subsequent motion of the object.

Repeat with objects of different mass and if possible with different liquids in the dashpot. Compare the types of motion that occur.

Now use the apparatus to investigate the following questions.

- Do oscillations always occur?
- If oscillations do occur, is their amplitude constant?
- If oscillations occur, is their period constant?
- If oscillations occur, does their rate of decay depend on the mass?

Figure 7.20

Design and carry out an experiment which will estimate the damping constant of the dashpot for two liquids such as water and oil.

1 A spring–mass oscillator consists of a spring with stiffness $20\,\text{Nm}^{-1}$ and an object of mass $0.25\,\text{kg}$. The object is pulled down $10\,\text{cm}$ from its equilibrium position and released.

(i) Formulate the differential equation and write down the initial conditions for the system, stating any modelling assumptions you make.

(ii) Find the particular solution describing the motion.

(iii) Sketch a graph of the solution.

A linear damping device is now introduced to the system.

(iv) Calculate the value of the damping constant if the system is to be critically damped.

(v) If the damping constant does not change, describe the motion of the system if

(a) the mass of the object is increased to $0.3\,\text{kg}$

(b) the mass of the object is decreased to $0.2\,\text{kg}$.

2 The pointer on a set of kitchen scales oscillates before settling down at its final reading.

If x is the reading at time t then the oscillation of the pointer is modelled by the differential equation

$$\frac{d^2x}{dt^2} + 3\frac{dx}{dt} + 10x = 0.5$$

(i) Find the general solution of the equation for x.

(ii) Given that $x = 0.1$ and $\frac{dx}{dt} = 0$ when $t = 0$, find the particular solution.

At what reading will the pointer settle?

(iii) What length of time will elapse before the amplitude of the oscillations of the pointer is less than 20% of the final value of x?

3 An electrical circuit consists of a 0.2 henry inductor, a 1 ohm resistor and a 0.8 farad capacitor in series. The charge q coulombs on the capacitor is modelled by the differential equation

$$0.2\frac{d^2q}{dt^2} + \frac{dq}{dt} + \frac{1}{0.8}q = 0.$$

Initially q is 2 and $\frac{dq}{dt}$ (the current in ampères) is 4.

(i) Find an equation for the charge as a function of time.

(ii) Sketch the graphs of charge and current against time. Describe how the charge and current change.

(iii) What is the charge on the capacitor and the current in the circuit after a long period of time?

4 The temperature of a chemical undergoing a reaction is modelled by the differential equation

$$2\frac{d^2T}{dt^2} + \frac{dT}{dt} = 0$$

where T is the temperature in °C and t is the time in minutes.

For a particular experiment, the temperature is initially 50°C, and it is 45°C one minute later.

(i) Find an expression for the temperature T at any time.

(ii) What will the temperature be after two minutes?

(iii) Sketch a graph of T against t.

(iv) What is the steady state temperature?

5 The angular displacement from its equilibrium position of a swing door fitted with a damping device is modelled by the differential equation

$$\frac{d^2\theta}{dt^2} + 4\frac{d\theta}{dt} + 5\theta = 0.$$

The door starts from rest at an angle of $\frac{\pi}{4}$ from its equilibrium position.

(i) Find the general solution of the differential equation.

(ii) Find the particular solution for the given initial conditions.

(iii) Sketch a graph of the particular solution, and hence describe the motion of the door.

(iv) What does your model predict as t becomes large?

6 A buffer on a railway truck consists of a spring and a damping device in parallel. The truck has mass 10 tonnes and collides with a rigid stop at a speed of $5\,\mathrm{ms}^{-1}$. The spring has stiffness $10^6\,\mathrm{Nm}^{-1}$ and the damping constant is $2 \times 10^5\,\mathrm{Nm}^{-1}\,\mathrm{s}$.

Assume that the buffer on the truck remains in contact with the rigid stop throughout the subsequent motion of the truck.

(i) Formulate and solve a differential equation to model the motion of the railway truck after the collision.

(ii) Sketch a graph of the solution, and from your graph describe the motion of the truck.

7 A simple model of a delicate set of laboratory scales comprises a spring of stiffness $5\,\mathrm{Nm}^{-1}$ and a damping device with constant $7\,\mathrm{Nm}^{-1}\,\mathrm{s}$. An object of mass m is placed carefully on the scales when the spring is unstretched. Take g to be $10\,\mathrm{ms}^{-2}$, and let x m be the displacement from the initial position.

(i) Formulate and solve a differential equation to model the motion of the object in each of the cases

    (a) $m = 2$

    (b) $m = 2.45$

    (c) $m = 4$.

(ii) Sketch a graph of the solution for objects of each value of m. Describe the motion in each case.

8 A hydrometer is an instrument used to measure the densities of liquids. It works on the principle that a floating body experiences an upthrust equal in magnitude to the weight of liquid displaced by that part of the body which is submerged.

A particular hydrometer consists of a light uniform cylindrical rod of radius a and length b with a small mass m countersunk into one end. In a liquid the hydrometer floats with its axis vertical and the amount by which it protrudes above the surface gives a measure of the density of the liquid.

Such a hydrometer floats in equilibrium in a liquid of density ρ with one quarter of its length above the surface.

(i) Find an expression for the density ρ in terms of a, b and m.

The hydrometer is pushed vertically downwards and then released. The resistance to motion when the speed is v is given by $2mkv$ where k is a constant. At time t the displacement of the equilibrium level below the surface is denoted by x. The differential equation governing the motion is $m\dfrac{\mathrm{d}^2x}{\mathrm{d}t^2} = -2mk\dfrac{\mathrm{d}x}{\mathrm{d}t} - \dfrac{4mg}{3b}x$.

(ii) Explain the physical significance of each of the three terms.

(iii) Show that for the hydrometer to perform damped simple harmonic motion

$$\frac{4g}{3b} > k^2.$$

Initially the hydrometer is pushed vertically downwards until just submerged and then released from rest.

(iv) Denoting $\dfrac{4g}{3b} - k^2$ by ω^2, solve the differential equation governing the motion and express the solution as an equation for x in terms of t, b, k and ω.

(v) Describe the motion of the hydrometer by sketching the graph of x against t.

Four complete oscillations after release, one eighth of the hydrometer is above the surface.

(vi) Show that the periodic time T of the oscillations is given by $T = \dfrac{\ln 2}{4k}$.

[MEI]

9 Many systems can be modelled by the non-homogeneous differential equation

$$\frac{d^2x}{dt^2} + \omega^2 x = c \qquad \textcircled{1}$$

where c is a constant.

(i) Show that introducing the new variable y, where $y = x - \dfrac{c}{\omega^2}$, gives the homogeneous differential equation

$$\frac{d^2y}{dt^2} + \omega^2 y = 0.$$

(ii) Hence write down the general solution of equation ①. Give a physical interpretation of the quantity $\dfrac{c}{\omega^2}$.

(iii) Use similar ideas to write down the general solution of the equation

$$\frac{d^2x}{dt^2} + r\frac{dx}{dt} + \omega^2 x = c$$

where $r > 0$ and c is a constant.

10 The diagram shows a block of mass $10\,\text{kg}$ being dragged across a horizontal surface by means of an elastic spring AB of unstretched length $0.5\,\text{m}$. The end A is being pulled with constant speed $5\,\text{ms}^{-1}$. The block is attached to the end B of the spring.

The block is subject to a resistance force given by $4v\,\text{N}$, where v is the speed of the block in ms^{-1}. The only other horizontal force acting on the block is the tension in the spring given by $T = k(y - 0.5)\,\text{N}$, where y is the length of the spring in metres and k is a constant (the stiffness of the spring).

(i) By considering the horizontal forces acting on the block, write down the equation of motion of the block in terms of $\dfrac{dv}{dt}$, v, y and k. Use the fact that $\dfrac{dy}{dt} = 5 - v$ to eliminate v, and show that

$$10\frac{d^2y}{dt^2} + 4\frac{dy}{dt} + ky = 0.5k + 20.$$

(ii) You are given that $k = 20$. Find the general solution of the differential equation.

At the beginning of the motion, the spring is unstretched and the block is at rest.

(iii) Find an expression for y at time $t > 0$.

(iv) What are the limiting values of v and y after a long period of time? Explain briefly how these values would be affected if a different spring were used with a lower value of k.

[MEI]

11 A ball is suspended vertically from one end of a spring. The other end is made to oscillate vertically and the ball is subject to air resistance. The differential equation modelling the motion is

$$\frac{d^2y}{dt^2} + 4\frac{dy}{dt} + 29y = 26\sin 5t,$$

where y is displacement and t is time.

(i) Find the general solution of the differential equation.

You are now given that, when $t = 0$, $y = -\dfrac{5}{6}$ and $\dfrac{dy}{dt} = 0$.

(ii) Find the solution subject to these conditions. Show that this solution can be expressed in the form

$$y = \tfrac{1}{12}(3 - e^{-2t})\,(\sin 5t - 5\cos 5t).$$

(iii) What is the smallest positive value of t for which $y = 0$?

(iv) Find the approximate amplitude of the oscillations for large values of t.

[MEI]

1 Motion for which the differential equation is $\frac{d^2x}{dt^2} + \omega^2 x = 0$ is called *simple harmonic motion* (SHM).

2 A spring–mass oscillator and a simple pendulum both perform SHM if friction and air resistance are negligible.

3 The period of this SHM is $T = \frac{2\pi}{\omega}$.

4 The angular frequency of the SHM is ω and the frequency is $v = \frac{\omega}{2\pi}$.

5 Linear damping is provided by a linear dashpot.

6 Motion for which the differential equation is

$$\frac{d^2x}{dt^2} + \alpha\frac{dx}{dt} + \omega^2 x = 0 \text{ (for } \alpha > 0)$$

is called *damped harmonic motion*. A spring–mass–dashpot system performs damped harmonic motion.

7 The following table shows the features of damped harmonic motion.

$\alpha^2 - 4\omega^2$	Solution	Type of damping
$\alpha = 0$	$x = A\sin\omega t + B\cos\omega t$ or $x = a\sin(\omega t + \varepsilon)$	no damping
positive $(\alpha > 2\omega)$	$x - Ae^{\lambda_1 t} + Be^{\lambda_2 t}$	overdamping
zero $(\alpha = 2\omega)$	$x = (A + Bt)e^{-\frac{\alpha t}{2}}$	critical damping
negative $(\alpha < 2\omega)$	$x = ae^{-\frac{\alpha t}{2}}\sin(\rho t + \varepsilon)$, where $\rho = \frac{1}{2}\sqrt{4\omega^2 - \alpha^2}$	underdamping

ⓔ Forced oscillations

One cannot escape the feeling that these mathematical formulae have an independent existence and an intelligence of their own, that they are wiser than we are, wiser even than their discoverers, that we get more out of them than was originally put into them.

Heinrich Hertz

ⓔ *This chapter is enrichment material.*

? Cleo Laine can break a wine glass by singing at it.

(i) How is it possible?

(ii) Can you do it?

All structures have natural frequencies of vibration. If an external agent causes them to vibrate at or near one of these frequencies, large oscillations are seen to build up. This phenomenon is called *resonance*. Over the years there have been several well-known instances of resonance occurring with dramatic and destructive effect.

- In 1963 a cooling tower at the Ferrybridge power station near Leeds collapsed. It had been caused to vibrate violently by vortices formed when the wind blew past a row of towers in front of it.
- In 1940 a wind of moderate speed caused large oscillations in the Takoma Narrows bridge in Washington, USA. The bridge eventually collapsed into the river below.

- In 1831 a column of soldiers marching over the Broughton suspension bridge, near Manchester, set up a forced vibration which had a frequency close to one of the natural frequencies of the bridge. The bridge collapsed. Since this disaster, it has become normal for troops to break step when crossing a bridge.
- In biblical times, after camping outside the walled town of Jericho for seven days, Joshua gave orders which brought the siege to an end in a curious way:

So they blew trumpets, and when the army heard the trumpet sound, they raised a great shout, and down came the walls.

Could this, too, have been the effect of forced vibrations?

These instances show how important it is for engineers to be able to predict the natural frequencies of any structures they are designing, and the frequencies of any possible forcing agents. Nor is this a matter for civil engineers alone: engines which run at particular frequencies cause ships and aircraft to shake themselves to pieces.

Modelling forced vibrations: the undamped case

In order to understand the mathematics of forced oscillations, including resonance, we look not at one of the complicated structures in the examples above, but at the simplest suitable case, that of an object hanging on a light, perfectly elastic spring, without damping. (The case in which both forcing and damping occur is considered in the second half of this chapter, on page 133.)

In figure 8.1 the top end A of the spring is forced to vibrate so that its displacement at time t is $y = a\sin\Omega t$. (This can be achieved experimentally, to a reasonable approximation, by attaching the supporting string over a pulley to a rotating cam, as shown in figure 8.5 on page 131.)

If the natural length of the spring is l_0, the stiffness of the spring is k and the object has mass m, then in equilibrium, point A coincides with O, the object is at rest and the extension of the spring is $e = \dfrac{mg}{k}$. At a general time t during the forced motion, the extension of the spring below the equilibrium position is denoted by x (figure 8.2).

Figure 8.1

Figure 8.2

There are two forces acting on the object, the force of gravity mg and the tension T. The acceleration of the object is $\dfrac{d^2x}{dt^2}$. Applying Newton's second law gives

$$m\frac{d^2x}{dt^2} = mg - T.$$

The extension of the spring is $(e + x - y)$, so the tension in the spring is

$$T = k(e + x - y).$$

The equation of motion is therefore

$$m\frac{d^2x}{dt^2} = mg - k(e + x - y).$$

Expanding the right-hand side and recalling that $mg - ke = 0$ (figure 8.1), this becomes

$$m\frac{d^2x}{dt^2} + kx = ky.$$

Dividing both sides by m and putting $\omega^2 = \dfrac{k}{m}$,

$$\frac{d^2x}{dt^2} + \omega^2 x = \omega^2 y \quad \text{or} \quad \frac{d^2x}{dt^2} + \omega^2 x = \omega^2 f(t) \qquad \text{①}$$

In the system we have described, $y = f(t) = a\sin\Omega t$. This is *forced harmonic motion*, and $\dfrac{\Omega}{2\pi}$ is called the forcing frequency. The differential equation of motion may be written

$$\frac{d^2x}{dt^2} + \omega^2 x = a\omega^2\sin\Omega t. \qquad \text{②}$$

The complementary function is given by

$$A\sin\omega t + B\cos\omega t.$$

For the particular integral, try $x = p\sin\Omega t + q\cos\Omega t$. This gives

$$\frac{dx}{dt} = p\Omega\cos\Omega t - q\Omega\sin\Omega t$$

and $\quad \dfrac{d^2x}{dt^2} = -p\Omega^2\sin\Omega t - q\Omega^2\cos\Omega t.$

> Normally you would use l and m in the trial function, but in this example p and q are used instead because l and m are representing length and mass.

Substituting these in the differential equation of motion gives

$$-p\Omega^2\sin\Omega t - q\Omega^2\cos\Omega t + p\omega^2\sin\Omega t + q\omega^2\cos\Omega t \equiv a\omega^2\sin\Omega t.$$

Equating coefficients:

$\sin\Omega t: \quad -p\Omega^2 + p\omega^2 = a\omega^2.$
$\cos\Omega t: \quad -q\Omega^2 + q\omega^2 = 0.$

Assuming $\Omega \neq \omega$, this gives $p = \dfrac{a\omega^2}{\omega^2 - \Omega^2}$ and $q = 0$.

The particular integral is therefore $\dfrac{a\omega^2}{\omega^2 - \Omega^2}\sin\Omega t.$

The general solution of the differential equation ② is therefore

$$x = A\sin\omega t + B\cos\omega t + \frac{a\omega^2}{\omega^2 - \Omega^2}\sin\Omega t \qquad (\Omega \neq \omega). \qquad \text{③}$$

? What is the physical significance of the terms

(i) $A\sin\omega t + B\cos\omega t$ **(ii)** $\dfrac{a\omega^2}{\omega^2 - \Omega^2}\sin\Omega t$

in the general solution above?

What would happen to the solution if Ω were increased steadily from zero towards ω?

Describing forced oscillations

You should have made the following deductions.

- The terms $A\sin\omega t + B\cos\omega t$ represent the natural or free oscillations of the system, as they would occur if the cam were not rotating. The natural frequency of the system is $\dfrac{\omega}{2\pi}$. You can see that these oscillations are as described for the spring–mass oscillator in Chapter 7.
- The term $\dfrac{a\omega^2}{\omega^2 - \Omega^2}\sin\Omega t$ represents the oscillations caused by the rotating cam.
- As the value of Ω approaches that of ω, the quantity $\omega^2 - \Omega^2$ in the denominator tends to zero: the forced oscillations increase in amplitude. Consequently a small input amplitude a leads to a much larger output amplitude $\dfrac{a\omega^2}{\omega^2 - \Omega^2}$. This effect is known as *resonance*.
- This solution is only valid in cases where Ω does not actually equal ω.

Over the last few pages we have set up and solved a differential equation to model a simple case of forced oscillations. This has given us a mathematical explanation for the phenomenon of resonance which we described at the start of this chapter.

The case when $\Omega = \omega$

Resonance occurs when the frequency of the driving function is the same as the natural frequency of the system. Looking back at the differential equation for the general spring–mass system (equation ② on page 127), this occurs when $\Omega = \omega$ and so the differential equation becomes

$$\frac{d^2x}{dt^2} + \omega^2 x = a\omega^2\sin\omega t.$$

Since it is unaffected by the function on the right-hand side of the equation, the complementary function is still $A\sin\omega t + B\cos\omega t$. To obtain the particular integral, given the function on the right-hand side, you would normally try $x = p\sin\omega t + q\cos\omega t$ but this is included in the complementary function. So you multiply the usual trial function by the independent variable.

In this case try $x = t(p\sin\omega t + q\cos\omega t)$.

Differentiating this gives

$$\frac{dx}{dt} = (p\sin\omega t + q\cos\omega t) + t(p\omega\cos\omega t - q\omega\sin\omega t)$$

and

$$\frac{d^2x}{dt^2} = p\omega\cos\omega t - q\omega\sin\omega t + p\omega\cos\omega t - q\omega\sin\omega t + t(-p\omega^2\sin\omega t - q\omega^2\cos\omega t)$$
$$= 2p\omega\cos\omega t - 2q\omega\sin\omega t - p\omega^2 t\sin\omega t - q\omega^2 t\cos\omega t.$$

Substituting these into the differential equation gives

$$2p\omega\cos\omega t - 2q\omega\sin\omega t - p\omega^2 t\sin\omega t - q\omega^2 t\cos\omega t + p\omega^2 t\sin\omega t$$
$$+ q\omega^2 t\cos\omega t \equiv a\omega^2\sin\omega t.$$

Equating coefficients:

$\sin\omega t$: $-2q\omega - p\omega^2 t + p\omega^2 t = a\omega^2$

$\Rightarrow$ $q = -\frac{1}{2}a\omega.$

$\cos\omega t$: $2p\omega - q\omega^2 t + q\omega^2 t = 0$

$\Rightarrow$ $p = 0.$

So a particular integral is $-\dfrac{a\omega t}{2}\cos\omega t$ and the general solution in the case when $\Omega = \omega$ is given by

This is called the forcing term.

$$x = A\sin\omega t + B\cos\omega t - \frac{a\omega t}{2}\cos\omega t.$$

Note that as t increases the forcing term dominates the solution. It represents an oscillation whose amplitude is proportional to t and so grows linearly with time. This is a mathematical description of resonance. It occurs when the forcing frequency is identical to the natural frequency of the system.

Drawing graphs of forced oscillations

To illustrate the general results we have just established, we take a particular set of values for the variables involved and specify the initial conditions.

The general solution of $\dfrac{d^2x}{dt^2} + \omega^2 x = a\omega^2\sin\Omega t$ for $\Omega \neq \omega$ is given by

$$x = A\sin\omega t + B\cos\omega t + \frac{a\omega^2}{\omega^2 - \Omega^2}\sin\Omega t$$

with $\omega = \sqrt{\dfrac{k}{m}}.$

We take the following values:

the stiffness of the spring: $k = 20\,\mathrm{Nm^{-1}}$
the mass of the object: $m = 0.2\,\mathrm{kg}$
the amplitude of the forcing motion: $a = 0.02\,\mathrm{m}$
acceleration due to gravity: $g = 10\,\mathrm{ms^{-2}}$,

and we assume that initially the object is stationary at the equilibrium position so that when $t = 0$, $x = 0$ and $\dfrac{dx}{dt} = 0$.

ACTIVITY

Show that under these circumstances the object's displacement, x, is given by

$$x = \frac{1}{(100 - \Omega^2)}(2\sin\Omega t - 0.2\Omega\sin 10t) \qquad (\Omega \neq 10).$$

The graphs in figure 8.3 show the variation of x with t for various values of Ω.

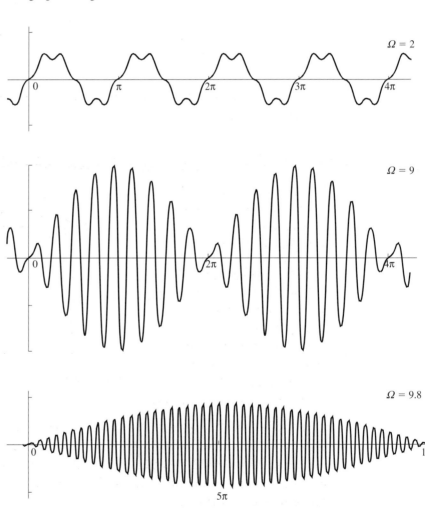

Figure 8.3

ACTIVITY

In the case when $\Omega = \omega$, the general solution was found to be

$$x = A\sin\omega t + B\cos\omega t - \frac{a\omega t}{2}\cos\omega t.$$

Show that with the values given on page 128, this result may be written as

$$x = 0.01\sin 10t - 0.1t\cos 10t$$

Figure 8.4 shows the graph of this solution.

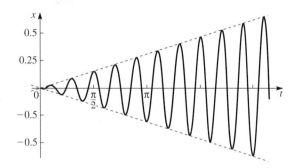

Figure 8.4

The experiment which follows will allow you to see how the theory we have just developed matches what happens in practice.

EXPERIMENT

Use apparatus as shown in figure 8.5 to investigate the effects of forced oscillations on a spring–mass oscillator.

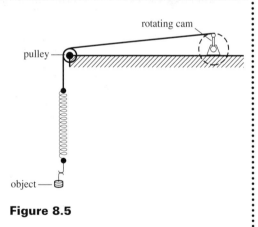

Figure 8.5

One end of the spring is attached to an object, and the other end is attached to an inelastic string passing over a pulley and tied to a peg on a rotating cam. You need to be able to run the motor at different speeds so that the cam rotates at a range of angular speeds.

As the cam rotates with a particular (constant) angular speed Ω, the top of the spring is forced to vibrate so that its displacement is $a\sin\Omega t$ where a and Ω are constants. Design and carry out an experiment to investigate the forced oscillations of the system with a range of forcing frequencies, and to demonstrate the occurrence of resonance.

Repeat the experiment with objects of different mass, and validate the result that the resonant frequency is proportional to $\sqrt{\dfrac{1}{m}}$.

1 A spring–mass system consists of a spring of natural length 0.5 m and stiffness 30 Nm^{-1} and an object of mass 0.6 kg. The system is placed horizontally on a smooth table, with one end attached to a point which is forced to vibrate so that its displacement is $y = 0.1\cos\Omega t$.

(i) Show that the position x of the object satisfies the differential equation

$$\frac{d^2x}{dt^2} + 50x = 25 + 5\cos\Omega t$$

(ii) If the object is initially at rest in its equilibrium position, find the particular solution for x, where $\Omega \neq \sqrt{50}$.

(iii) Use a graphics calculator or computer to draw the graph of the function x for different values of Ω. Describe the motion of the object.

(iv) State the value of Ω for which resonance occurs. Find the particular solution for x in this case, and sketch its graph.

2 An electrical circuit consists of a 1 henry inductor and a 10^{-4} F capacitor in series with a sinusoidal power source.

The charge q, in coulombs (C), stored in the capacitor is given by the differential equation

$$\frac{d^2q}{dt^2} + 10\,000q = 1000\sin\Omega t$$

where t is the time in seconds. Initially the charge q and current $\frac{dq}{dt}$ in the circuit are both zero.

(i) Find the particular solution for the charge q.

(ii) State the value of Ω for which resonance occurs. Find the particular solution for $q(t)$ in this case. Calculate the time at which the charge first exceeds 10 000 C.

(iii) Use a graphics calculator or computer to graph the solution in part (ii).

3 An oscillatory system with negligible damping is forced to vibrate by a periodic force of constant amplitude F and frequency $\frac{p}{2\pi}$. The displacement y of the system from its equilibrium position satisfies the differential equation

$$\frac{d^2y}{dt^2} + \omega^2 y = \omega^2 F\sin pt.$$

(i) Find the general solution of this equation.

(ii) Obtain the particular solution for which $y = 1$ and $\frac{dy}{dt} = 0$ when $t = 0$.

(iii) Use a graphic calculator or computer to draw the graph of the particular solution for $F = 1$ and $p = \pi$ in the cases when
(a) $\omega = 0.5\pi$ and **(b)** $\omega = 0.9\pi$.
Describe what happens as ω approaches π.

(iv) Show that if $\omega \approx p$ then, to a good approximation, the particular solution becomes

$$y = \cos\omega t + \frac{F}{2}\sin\omega t - \frac{\omega Ft}{2}\cos\omega t.$$

Damped forced oscillations

In Chapter 7 you saw the effect on simple harmonic motion of introducing a linear damping device called a dashpot. The oscillations, if they occurred, decayed to zero. If the damping constant r was large compared with the stiffness of the spring and the mass of the object, oscillations did not occur at all.

Earlier in this chapter you have seen the effect of forcing an undamped system. Most real systems do have an element of damping, so in this section we explore the effect of including a linear dashpot in the system. To make comparison easy, we shall look again at the spring–mass oscillator with the values given on page 130.

Figure 8.6 shows the spring–mass system which, as before, is forced to oscillate. A linear dashpot has been added below the object.

As before, the spring has stiffness $20\,\mathrm{Nm^{-1}}$, the object has mass $0.2\,\mathrm{kg}$ and the amplitude of the forcing oscillation is 2 cm. The dashpot constant is $1\,\mathrm{Nm^{-1}s}$ and g is taken to be $10\,\mathrm{ms^{-2}}$. The object starts from rest in its equilibrium position.

dashpot

Figure 8.6

The first step is to formulate a differential equation to model this system.

Figure 8.7 shows the system and the forces acting, first in equilibrium and then at some general time t during the motion.

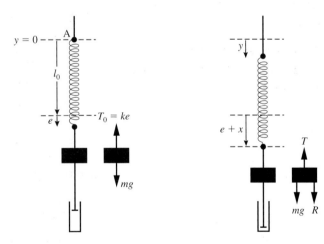

Figure 8.7

In equilibrium, the extension of the spring is $e = \dfrac{mg}{k} = \dfrac{2}{20} = 0.1$. At the general time t the object is displaced a distance x below the equilibrium level. The acceleration of the object is $\dfrac{\mathrm{d}^2x}{\mathrm{d}t^2}$.

The net force on the object in the direction of positive x (i.e. downwards) is $mg + R - T$.

Applying Newton's second law at any instant t gives

$$m\frac{d^2x}{dt^2} = mg + R - T.$$

The extension of the spring is $e + x - y$ so $T = 20(0.1 + x - y)$.

Let the length of the dashpot at time t be L, and its length in equilibrium be L_0. Then $L = L_0 - x$, and $\frac{dL}{dt} = -\frac{dx}{dt}$.

The dashpot force R is given by $r\frac{dL}{dt}$, where r is the dashpot constant. So in this case,

$$R = 1\frac{dL}{dt} = -\frac{dx}{dt}.$$

The equation of motion becomes

> This is mg.

$$0.2\frac{d^2x}{dt^2} = 2 - \frac{dx}{dt} - 20(0.1 + x - y)$$

$$\Rightarrow \quad \frac{d^2x}{dt^2} + 5\frac{dx}{dt} + 100x = 100y.$$

If the displacement of the forcing point is $y = 0.02\sin\Omega t$, the differential equation modelling the system is

$$\frac{d^2y}{dt^2} + 5\frac{dx}{dt} + 100x = 2\sin\Omega t.$$

The next stage is to solve the differential equation, which is (as before) a non-homogeneous linear equation with constant coefficients. Its auxiliary equation is

$$\lambda^2 + 5\lambda + 100 = 0$$

whose roots are

$$\lambda = \frac{-5 \pm \sqrt{375}j}{2}$$

$$\Rightarrow \quad \lambda = -2.5 \pm 9.68j.$$

The complementary function is therefore $e^{-2.5t}(A\sin 9.68t + B\cos 9.68t)$.

For the particular integral, try $x = p\sin\Omega t + q\cos\Omega t$.

Differentiating this gives

$$\frac{dx}{dt} = p\Omega\cos\Omega t - q\Omega\sin\Omega t$$

and $\quad \dfrac{d^2x}{dt^2} = -p\Omega^2\sin\Omega t - q\Omega^2\cos\Omega t.$

Substituting these in the differential equation for the system, gives

$$-p\Omega^2\sin\Omega t - q\Omega^2\cos\Omega t + 5p\Omega\cos\Omega t - 5q\Omega\sin\Omega t + 100p\sin\Omega t + 100q\cos\Omega t$$
$$\equiv 2\sin\Omega t.$$

Equating coefficients:

$\sin\Omega t$: $-p\Omega^2 - 5q\Omega + 100p = 2.$
$\cos\Omega t$: $-q\Omega^2 + 5p\Omega + 100q = 0.$

Solving these equations for p and q gives

$$p = \frac{2(100 - \Omega^2)}{(100 - \Omega^2)^2 + 25\Omega^2}$$

and $$q = -\frac{10\Omega}{(100 - \Omega^2)^2 + 25\Omega^2}.$$

The particular integral is therefore

$$\frac{2(100 - \Omega^2)}{(100 - \Omega^2)^2 + 25\Omega^2}\sin\Omega t - \frac{10\Omega}{(100 - \Omega^2)^2 + 25\Omega^2}\cos\Omega t.$$

The general solution is the sum of the complementary function and the particular integral:

$$x = e^{-2.5t}(A\sin9.68t + B\cos9.68t) + \frac{2(100 - \Omega^2)}{(100 - \Omega^2)^2 + 25\Omega^2}\sin\Omega t$$
$$- \frac{10\Omega}{(100 - \Omega^2)^2 + 25\Omega^2}\cos\Omega t.$$

As t increases, the natural damped oscillations, given by the complementary function, decay because of the $e^{-2.5t}$ term, leaving

$$x = \frac{2(100 - \Omega^2)}{(100 - \Omega^2)^2 + 25\Omega^2}\sin\Omega t - \frac{10\Omega}{(100 - \Omega^2)^2 + 25\Omega^2}\cos\Omega t.$$

This is called the *steady state* solution. It is the particular integral of the differential equation. It describes the oscillations that occur after the unforced oscillations have died away. Figure 8.8 shows graphs of this steady state solution for two values of Ω.

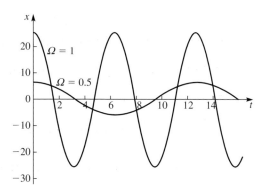

Figure 8.8

Remember that in the undamped case the value of Ω for resonance was calculated by setting the denominator to zero in the particular integral. Catastrophic resonance does not occur in the damped case, because the denominator of each part of the particular integral is always greater than zero. However, the amplitude of the forced vibrations does still depend on the value of Ω.

The amplitude of the steady state oscillations is the square root of the sum of the squares of the coefficients of $\cos\Omega t$ and $\sin\Omega t$ in the steady state solution, i.e.

$$\sqrt{\left(\frac{2(100 - \Omega^2)}{(100 - \Omega^2)^2 + 25\Omega^2}\right)^2 + \left(\frac{-10\Omega}{(100 - \Omega^2)^2 + 25\Omega^2}\right)^2}.$$

This can be simplified to $\dfrac{2}{\sqrt{(100 - \Omega^2)^2 + 25\Omega^2}}$.

This result shows how the amplitude of the steady state solution depends on Ω. Figure 8.9 shows a graph of this amplitude against Ω.

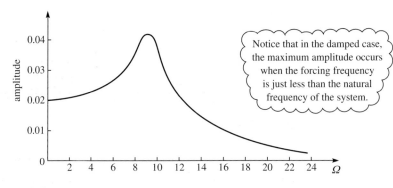

Figure 8.9

When Ω and ω are close in value to each other, then it follows that the forcing frequency $\dfrac{\Omega}{2\pi}$ and the natural frequency $\dfrac{\omega}{2\pi}$ are close in value. When this is the case, the steady state oscillations become large compared with the input amplitude a. The motion of the system at these relatively large amplitudes is still called resonance, though the amplitude of the vibrations does not increase without limit as it does in the undamped case.

You have now seen the effect of linear damping on the system. What would be the effect of varying the damping constant, r? To predict this, look at the differential equation for the same damped spring–mass system ($m = 0.2$ and $k = 20$), but this time use a general damping constant r. The equation becomes

$$0.2\frac{d^2x}{dt^2} + r\frac{dx}{dt} + 20x = 0.4\sin\Omega t.$$

We know that the complementary function decays and that the steady state oscillations are given by the particular integral. In this case it is

$$x = \frac{0.4(20 - 0.2\Omega^2)}{(20 - 0.2\Omega^2)^2 + r^2\Omega^2} \sin\Omega t - \frac{0.4r\Omega}{(20 - 0.2\Omega^2)^2 + r^2\Omega^2} \cos\Omega t.$$

The amplitude of the steady state forced oscillation is

$$\frac{2}{\sqrt{(100 - \Omega^2)^2 + 25r^2\Omega^2}}.$$

Figure 8.10 shows graphs of the steady state amplitude against Ω for different values of r.

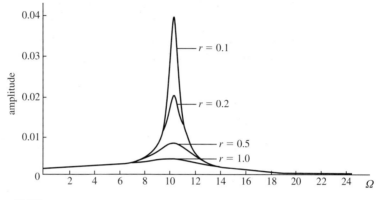

Figure 8.10

The graphs show that as r decreases (i.e. the amount of damping is reduced), the amplitude at the resonant frequency increases. In each case resonance occurs when Ω is very near in value to ω (in this case 10). In any real system there is always some damping but, as you can see, if the damping constant is small the resonance can still be damaging.

ACTIVITY

The previous example involved a particular case of damped forced motion in which the various parameters of the system were given particular values.

(i) Show that the differential equation modelling the general case may be written

$$\frac{d^2x}{dt^2} + \alpha\frac{dx}{dt} + \omega^2x = a\omega^2\sin\Omega t$$

(ii) Find **(a)** the general solution;

(b) the particular solution corresponding to

$$x = 0 \text{ and } \frac{dx}{dt} = 0 \text{ at } t = 0;$$

(c) the amplitude of the steady state oscillations.

1 The diagram shows a damped spring–mass system consisting of a particle of mass 1 kg oscillating on a smooth horizontal air track connected by a spring of stiffness $10\,\mathrm{Nm^{-1}}$, natural length 1 m, to a fixed point O. The particle is attached to a forcing point A via a dashpot of constant $3\,\mathrm{Nm^{-1}s}$. The displacement of point A from the fixed point O is $y(t)$.

(i)   Show that the displacement x of the particle satisfies the differential equation

$$\frac{d^2x}{dt^2} + 3\frac{dx}{dt} + 10x = 10 + 3\frac{dy}{dt}.$$

(ii) If the forcing function is $y = 2 + 0.1\cos2t$, and the particle starts from rest at $x = 1$, find the particular solution of the differential equation.

(iii) Use a graphics calculator or computer to draw graphs of x and y against t on the same axes.

2 The current I amperes in an electric circuit (consisting of inductance and resistance in series with a sinusoidal power source) is given by the differential equation

$$\frac{dI}{dt} + 2I = \sin3t,$$

where t is the elapsed time in seconds. Find

(i)   the complementary function
(ii) the particular integral
(iii) the current I as a function of time t, given that initially $I = 0$
(iv) the amplitude of the oscillations of the current after a long time has elapsed.

[MEI]

3 The forced oscillations of a damped harmonic system are modelled by the differential equation

$$\frac{d^2x}{dt^2} + 2\frac{dx}{dt} + 10x = \sin\omega t.$$

(i)   Find the complementary function of this differential equation.
(ii) Hence determine the nature of the damping.
(iii) Find the particular integral.
(iv) Show that the amplitude of the oscillations of the system when t is large is given approximately by

$$\frac{1}{\sqrt{(10 - \omega^2)^2 + 4\omega^2}}.$$

[MEI]

4 An electrical circuit consists of a 100 ohm resistor, a 1 henry inductor and a 10^{-4} farad capacitor in series with a sinusoidal power source. The charge q coulombs stored in the capacitor at time t is given by the differential equation

$$\frac{d^2q}{dt^2} + 100\frac{dq}{dt} + 10\,000q = 1000\sin100t$$

where t is the time in seconds.

(i)   Find the complementary function of the differential equation.
(ii) Decide if the circuit is overdamped, critically damped or underdamped.
(iii) Find the particular integral and hence the general solution.
(iv) Initially both q and $\dfrac{dq}{dt}$, the current in the circuit, are zero. Find the values of the unknown constants in the general solution.
(v)   Use a graphics calculator or computer to sketch the solution and describe how the charge in the circuit changes with time.

5 (i)   Find the general solution of the simple harmonic differential equation

$$\ddot{x} + \omega^2x = 0.$$

(ii) Comparing each of the following differential equations with the one above, give in each case a physical interpretation of the extra term.

$$\ddot{x} + k\dot{x} + \omega^2x = 0, \quad k > 0,$$
$$\ddot{x} + \omega^2x = A\cos\alpha t$$

(iii) Solve the second differential equation in part (ii) for $\alpha \neq \omega$.

(iv) Explain what happens to your solution as α approaches the value of ω.

[MEI]

6 A sphere of mass m and radius a is falling vertically through a liquid which produces a linear resistance force. The motion of the sphere is modelled by the differential equation

$$m\frac{d^2x}{dt^2} + ra\frac{dx}{dt} = mg$$

where x is the distance fallen in t seconds and r is a constant. The sphere is released from rest so that $x = 0$ and $\frac{dx}{dt} = 0$ when $t = 0$.

(i) Find the solution for x and hence the velocity of the sphere as a function of time.

(ii) Draw a graph of the velocity against time, and describe the motion of the sphere.

7 During the design of a car, part of the suspension system is tested by subjecting it to violent displacements. One such test is modelled by the differential equation

$$\ddot{x} + 2k\dot{x} + x = 1$$

where x is displacement, and initially $x = 0$ and $\dot{x} = 0$. The parameter $k\,(>0)$ is known as the damping coefficient and can be varied during the tests.

For optimum road holding a 'hard' suspension is desirable and it is believed that to achieve this the damping should be critical.

(i) Find the value of k for critical damping.

(ii) Determine x as a function of time t in this case.

For a more comfortable ride a 'soft' suspension is proposed in which $k = 0.6$.

(iii) Determine x as a function of time t for the 'soft' suspension.

(iv) Find the maximum displacement of the 'soft' suspension.

[MEI]

8 The current in an electrical circuit consisting of an inductor, resistor and capacitor in series with an alternating power source, is described by the equation

$$\frac{d^2I}{dt^2} + 25\frac{dI}{dt} + 100I = -170\sin 20t$$

where I is the current in amperes and t is the time in seconds after the power source is switched on.

(i) Find the general solution.

When $t = 0$, $\frac{dI}{dt} = I = 0$.

(ii) Find the solution.

The exponentially decaying terms in the solution describe what is known as the transient current. The non-decaying terms describe the steady state current.

(iii) Write down an expression for the steady state current for the solution in part (ii). Why would this expression remain unchanged if the initial conditions were different?

(iv) Express the steady state current in the form $R\sin(20t + \alpha)$, where R and α are to be determined. Verify that, after only 1 second, the magnitude of the transient current is close to 1% of the steady state amplitude, R.

[MEI]

9 In a simulation, a piece of machinery is subjected to vibrations of the form $a\sin\omega t$ to test the behaviour of one of the components. Different values of ω are used in different tests. The component is not subject to any damping. The displacement, x cm, of the component can be modelled by

$$\ddot{x} + 196x = 2\sin\omega t$$

where t is the time in seconds.

(i) Find the complementary function.

(ii) In the case $\omega \neq 14$, find a particular integral of the form $\lambda\sin\omega t + \mu\cos\omega t$, where λ and μ are to be found in terms of ω. Hence write down the general solution of the differential equation.

(iii) In the case $\omega = 14$:

    (a) Why will a particular integral of the form given in part (ii) not satisfy the differential equation? In this case, find the particular integral and hence write down the general solution of the differential equation.

    (b) Find the solution satisfying $\dot{x} = x = 0$ when $t = 0$. Describe the nature of the oscillations.

                              [MEI]

10 One end of a light spring is initially fixed at a point O and a particle of mass 2 kg is attached at the other end of the spring which hangs vertically beneath O. The tension in the spring is $50(x + 0.392)$ newtons, where x metres is the displacement of the particle below the equilibrium position.

The particle is held at a point 0.2 m below the equilibrium position and when $t = 0$ it is released from rest.

(i) Show that the motion of the particle may be modelled by the simple harmonic motion equation

$$\ddot{x} + 25x = 0.$$

(ii) Write down the general solution of this equation. Find the particular solution in this case.

The upper end of the spring is made to oscillate about O. The motion of the particle is now modelled by the differential equation

$$\ddot{x} + 25x = 0.5 \sin 5t.$$

When $t = 0$, $x = 0$ and the particle is at rest.

(iii) Solve the differential equation to find x in terms of t. Describe briefly the motion of the particle.

The particle is now submerged in liquid in order to damp the oscillations. The motion of the particle is now modelled by the differential equation

$$\ddot{x} + k\dot{x} + 25x = 0.5 \sin 5t,$$

where k is a constant.

(iv) Explain why k must be positive. For what range of values of k will the system be underdamped?

                              [MEI]

INVESTIGATIONS

Oscillations of a mass–pulley system

Figure 8.11 shows a simple mass–pulley system.

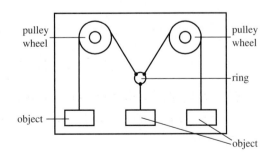

Figure 8.11

Investigate the motion of the three objects when the central object is displaced from its equilibrium position.

Can the motion of the central object be described as damped simple harmonic motion?

Electric circuit

Set up a circuit in which an inductor, a capacitor and a resistor are in series with an applied voltage. Investigate and analyse the behaviour when the voltage is provided by

(i) a sequence generator
(ii) a variable frequency oscillator.

KEY POINTS

e Motion for which the differential equation is $\dfrac{d^2x}{dt^2} + \omega^2 x = \omega^2 f(t)$ is called undamped forced harmonic motion; $f(t)$ is the forcing term. For a sinusoidal forcing term, $f(t) = a\sin\Omega t$ and the general solution of the differential equation is

$$x = A\sin\omega t + B\cos\omega t + \frac{a\omega^2}{\omega^2 - \Omega^2}\sin\Omega t \qquad (\omega \neq \Omega).$$

e The quantity $\dfrac{\Omega}{2\pi}$ is called the forcing frequency, and $\dfrac{\omega}{2\pi}$ is the natural frequency of the system. When $\Omega = \omega$ resonance occurs. In this case $f(t) = a\sin\omega t$ and the general solution is

$$x = A\sin\omega t + B\cos\omega t - \frac{a\omega t}{2}\cos\omega t.$$

e With linear damping, the differential equation model becomes

$$\frac{d^2x}{dt^2} + \alpha\frac{dx}{dt} + \omega^2 x = a\omega^2\sin\Omega t \qquad (\alpha > 0).$$

e The complementary function of this differential equation decays to zero. The particular integral remains and is called the *steady state* solution. If $f(t) = a\sin\Omega t$ then the steady state solution is

$$x = \frac{(\omega^2 - \Omega^2)a\omega^2}{(\omega^2 - \Omega^2)^2 + \Omega^2\alpha^2}\sin\Omega t - \frac{a\alpha\Omega\omega^2}{(\omega^2 - \Omega^2)^2 + \Omega^2\alpha^2}\cos\Omega t.$$

e The amplitude of this steady state solution is

$$\frac{a\omega^2}{\sqrt{(\omega^2 - \Omega^2)^2 + \Omega^2\alpha^2}}.$$

e When Ω takes the value which maximises the amplitude of the steady state oscillations, $\dfrac{\Omega}{2\pi}$ is called the *resonant frequency*.

9

Systems of differential equations

What's lost upon the roundabout
We pulls up on the swings!

Patrick Reginald Chambers

The photograph shows a typical Los Angeles smog, caused largely by exhaust fumes from motor vehicles. This smog, like almost all forms of man-made pollution, constitutes a health hazard to those who are exposed to it. The routes by which noxious pollutants enter human beings often involve several stages, for example a food chain.

Consequently when formulating differential equations to model such processes, you are likely to require a number of variables, a *system*. This is illustrated by the following example, which is based on studies into the effects of lead pollution on people living and working in Los Angeles. You should however realise from the outset that systems of differential equations may be applied to many different situations; modelling pollution is just one example.

Lead enters the body via food, air and water. It builds up in the blood, in body tissues and in the bones. Lead can leave the body via urine, hair, nails, skin and sweat, but enough can remain to present a significant health risk. It takes longer for lead to get into the bones than into the blood and the body tissue, but once there it is harder to remove and is particularly harmful. We shall concentrate first on the lead building up in the blood and body tissue.

If we represent the blood and body tissue as two separate compartments in a diagram, and show by arrows the possible transfers of lead into and out of each compartment, we can build up what is called a *compartmental model* (figure 9.1).

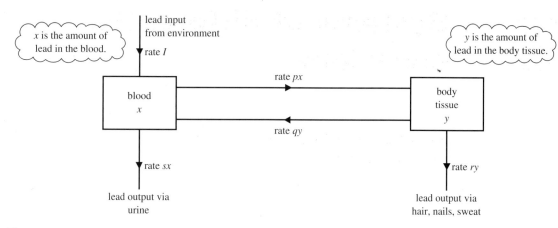

Figure 9.1

Biological research shows that it is reasonable to assume that the rate of transfer of lead from one part of the body to another is proportional to the amount of lead present. The symbols p, q, r and s are the constants of proportionality for the routes shown in figure 9.1.

A mathematical model can be built up for this system. Take the blood first, at any time t:

rate of increase of lead in bloodstream = rate of input − rate of output.

Expressing this mathematically using the notation in the flowchart,

$$\frac{dx}{dt} = (I + qy) - (px + sx)$$
$$= I - (p + s)x + qy.$$

Similarly for the body tissue

$$\frac{dy}{dt} = px - qy - ry$$
$$= px - (q + r)y.$$

We now have two differential equations, both involving the dependent variables x and y and the independent variable t. When two or more differential equations involve the same combination of variables they are called a *system* of differential equations. In this case, since both of the equations are linear, we have a linear system. In this chapter you will meet methods of solving linear systems of differential equations analytically.

Solving linear simultaneous differential equations

Before taking the example of lead pollution further, we take a simple numerical example to show how linear first order differential equations may be solved.

To see the method of approach, look at the pair of equations

$$\frac{dx}{dt} = 2x + 4y \qquad \qquad ①$$

$$\frac{dy}{dt} = x - y \qquad \qquad ②$$

with initial conditions $x = 2$ and $y = -2$ when $t = 0$.

Start by making x the subject in equation ② (since this is the simpler equation):

$$x = \frac{dy}{dt} + y \qquad \qquad ③$$

Now differentiate both sides with respect to t to obtain

$$\Rightarrow \qquad \frac{dx}{dt} = \frac{d^2y}{dt^2} + \frac{dy}{dt}.$$

Substituting for x and $\frac{dx}{dt}$ in equation ① gives

$$\frac{d^2y}{dt^2} + \frac{dy}{dt} = 2\left(\frac{dy}{dt} + y\right) + 4y.$$

This simplifies to the second order differential equation with constant coefficients:

$$\frac{d^2y}{dt^2} - \frac{dy}{dt} - 6y = 0. \qquad \qquad ④$$

This equation involves only one of the dependent variables, in this case y but not x. We can apply standard techniques to solve this.

The auxiliary equation is $\lambda^2 - \lambda - 6 = 0$ which has roots $\lambda = 3$ and $\lambda = -2$.

The general solution of equation ④ is therefore

$$y = Ae^{3t} + Be^{-2t}.$$

Substituting this into equation ③ gives the general solution for x:

$$x = 4Ae^{3t} - Be^{-2t}.$$

We now have the general solution, since we have an expression for x in terms of t and a separate expression for y in terms of t.

To find the values of the unknown constants of integration A and B we use the given initial conditions:

$$t = 0, x = 2 \qquad \Rightarrow \qquad 2 = 4A - B$$
$$t = 0, y = -2 \qquad \Rightarrow \qquad -2 = A + B$$

Solving for A and B gives $A = 0$ and $B = -2$.

The particular solution of the system of equations ① and ② satisfying the given initial conditions is

$$x = 2e^{-2t}$$
$$y = -2e^{-2t}.$$

Both x and y tend to zero as t tends to infinity. Figure 9.2 shows the behaviour of the solution graphically.

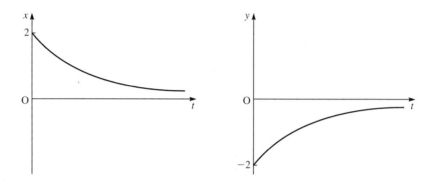

Figure 9.2

Sometimes it is important to understand the relationship between x and y, in which case the solution can be thought of as a pair of parametric equations with parameter t. In the example above t can be eliminated simply by adding the two solutions:

$$x = 2e^{-t}$$
$$\underline{y = -2e^{-t}}$$
$$x + y = 0.$$

This is illustrated in figure 9.3. Notice that only part of the line $x + y = 0$ is required, since the starting point is $x = -2$, $y = 2$ and as $t \to \infty$, $(x, y) \to (0, 0)$.

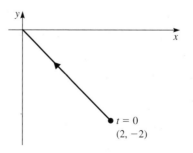

Figure 9.3

A graph like this is called a *solution curve*. It shows the relationship between the dependent variables (in this case x and y) as the independent variable (in this case t) increases through its permitted range.

EXAMPLE 9.1

(i) Find the general solution of the system of differential equations

$$\frac{dx}{dt} = -3y \qquad \qquad ①$$

$$\frac{dy}{dt} = 3x. \qquad \qquad ②$$

(ii) Find the particular solution given that $x = 3$, $y = 4$ when $t = 0$.

(iii) Sketch graphs of x and y against time t, and of y against x (the solution curve) for this particular solution. Describe the behaviour of the system.

SOLUTION

(i) From equation ②

$$x = \frac{1}{3}\frac{dy}{dt}.$$

Differentiating this gives

$$\frac{dx}{dt} = \frac{1}{3}\frac{d^2y}{dt^2}.$$

Substituting for $\frac{dx}{dt}$ in equation ① gives a second order differential equation with constant coefficients:

$$\frac{d^2y}{dt^2} = -9y.$$

You will recognise this as the equation of simple harmonic motion with general solution

$$y = A\sin 3t + B\cos 3t.$$

Substituting for y in equation ② gives the general solution for x:

$$x = A\cos 3t - B\sin 3t.$$

(ii) Applying the given boundary conditions

$$x = 3, \, t = 0 \quad \Rightarrow \quad 3 = A$$
$$y = 4, \, t = 0 \quad \Rightarrow \quad 4 = B,$$

the particular solution is

$$x = 3\cos 3t - 4\sin 3t$$
$$y = 3\sin 3t + 4\cos 3t.$$

(iii) The graphs of x and y against time t are shown in figure 9.4.

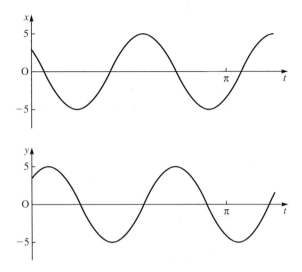

Figure 9.4

These solutions show that x and y are periodic functions of time with the same period, $\dfrac{2\pi}{3}$. Both x and y have amplitude $\sqrt{3^2 + 4^2} = 5$, but they are out of phase. The solution of the curve is a circle of radius 5, as shown in figure 9.5.

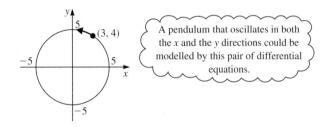

Figure 9.5

EXAMPLE 9.2

A system of differential equations is given by

$$\frac{dx}{dt} = -x + y - 1 \qquad \qquad ①$$

$$\frac{dy}{dt} = -x - y + 3. \qquad \qquad ②$$

When $t = 0$, $x = 0$ and $y = 3$.

(i) Find expressions for x and y in terms of t.

(ii) Draw the graph of y against x for values of $t \geqslant 0$. Describe what happens as $t \to \infty$.

SOLUTION

(i) Equation ① gives

$$y = x + \frac{dx}{dt} + 1.$$ ③

Differentiating this to find an expression for $\frac{dy}{dt}$ gives

$$\frac{dy}{dt} = \frac{dx}{dt} + \frac{d^2x}{dt^2}.$$

Substituting for y and $\frac{dy}{dt}$ in equation ② gives

$$\frac{dx}{dt} + \frac{d^2x}{dt^2} = -x - \left(x + \frac{dx}{dt} + 1\right) + 3.$$

Rearranging this, you find that the pair of first order differential equations gives rise to a second order differential equation with constant coefficients:

$$\frac{d^2x}{dt^2} + 2\frac{dx}{dt} + 2x = 2.$$

As you may verify, the general solution of this equation is

$$x = Ae^{-t}\sin t + Be^{-t}\cos t + 1.$$

Substituting for x and $\frac{dx}{dt}$ in equation ③ gives the general solution for y:

$$y = Ae^{-t}\cos t - Be^{-t}\sin t + 2.$$

The initial conditions give the values of A and B:

when $t = 0$, $x = 0$ $\Rightarrow$ $0 = B + 1$ $\Rightarrow$ $B = -1$;
when $t = 0$, $y = 3$ $\Rightarrow$ $3 = A + 2$ $\Rightarrow$ $A = 1$.

The particular solution that satisfies the initial conditions is therefore

$$x = e^{-t}\sin t - e^{-t}\cos t + 1$$
$$y = e^{-t}\cos t + e^{-t}\sin t + 2.$$

(ii) Figure 9.6 shows the graph of y against x.

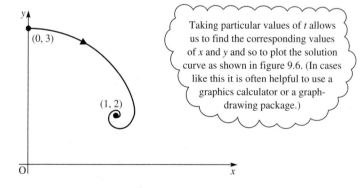

Taking particular values of t allows us to find the corresponding values of x and y and so to plot the solution curve as shown in figure 9.6. (In cases like this it is often helpful to use a graphics calculator or a graph-drawing package.)

Figure 9.6

As t increases, $e^{-t} \rightarrow 0$, so $x \rightarrow 1$ and $y \rightarrow 2$. In the long term the system approaches the point $(1, 2)$.

Solving the lead absorption equations

You now have the techniques to solve the system of equations on page 143 which were developed to model lead absorption and clearance by the human body. The equations are

$$\frac{dx}{dt} = I - (p + s)x + qy$$

$$\frac{dy}{dt} = px - (q + r)y.$$

In a heavy smog in Los Angeles, the intake of lead can be 50 µg per day, so $I = 50$. Data for an average-sized teenager give the following values: $p = 0.01$, $q = 0.01$, $r = 0.02$ and $s = 0.02$, where the masses are in micrograms (µg) and time is in days. Substituting these into the differential equations gives

$$\frac{dx}{dt} = 50 - 0.03x + 0.01y \qquad \qquad ①$$

$$\frac{dy}{dt} = 0.01x - 0.03y. \qquad \qquad ②$$

By eliminating y between the two equations you find that x satisfies the second order differential equation

$$100\frac{d^2x}{dt^2} + 6\frac{dx}{dt} + 0.08x = 150.$$

The general solution of this equation is

$$x = Ae^{-0.04t} + Be^{-0.02t} + 1875.$$

Substituting for x into ① gives

$$y = -Ae^{-0.04t} + Be^{-0.02t} + 625.$$

Figure 9.7 shows graphs of x and y against t for someone arriving in Los Angeles from a totally unpolluted area. The limiting values of x and y are 1875 and 625. What this means is that a constant input of 50 µg per day will eventually lead to a steady level of lead in the blood of 1875 µg and a steady level of lead in the body tissue of 625 µg.

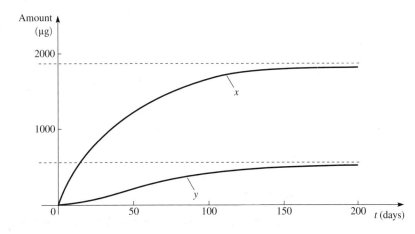

Figure 9.7

ACTIVITY

Lead can also be transferred between the blood and the bones. The rate of input to the bones is ux, and the rate of output from the bones is vz, where z is the amount of lead in the bones. Typical values for u and v are 0.004 and 0.000 035. You can assume the amount of lead transferred directly between the bones and the body tissue to be zero.

Extend the model formulated above to include a third compartment, the bones. You will now need three differential equations.

Equilibrium points

In the example of lead pollution, we found that the levels in the blood and tissue settled on steady equilibrium values of 1875 μg and 625 μg. Many systems settle to such equilibrium (or stationary) points. In the case of lead build-up in the human body, an equilibrium point corresponds physically to the amount of lead remaining constant in both the blood and the body tissue. For this balance to remain, the net exchange between the blood and the body tissue must be zero and the total amount of lead entering the body must be equal to the amount leaving the body.

It is useful to think of the state of a system at any instant being represented by the position of a particle as it travels along the solution curve. Each point on a solution curve has co-ordinates that are the values of x and y corresponding to a particular value of t. The curve starts at the point corresponding to the initial conditions. It finishes at the co-ordinates that correspond either to the limit as $t \rightarrow \infty$ or to some other specified end instant. It is important to realise that there is a *direction* associated with a solution curve: the behaviour of the system is described by the path of the curve from the start point to the end point (i.e. in the direction in which time increases). It is usual to indicate this by an arrow.

Equilibrium points can usually best be seen by drawing the family of solution curves for the general solution. The three other examples used so far in this chapter all included a drawing of a particular solution curve; the graphs below show the families of solution curves for their general solutions.

Case 1

$$\frac{dx}{dt} = 2x + 4y$$

$$\frac{dy}{dt} = x - y$$

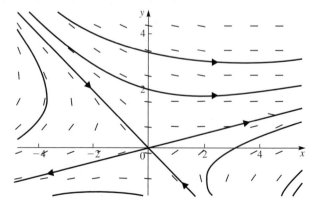

Figure 9.8

Case 2

$$\frac{dx}{dt} = -3y$$

$$\frac{dy}{dt} = 3x$$

Figure 9.9

Case 3

$$\frac{dx}{dt} = -x + y - 1$$

$$\frac{dy}{dt} = -x - y + 3$$

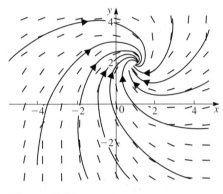

Figure 9.10

You will see from looking at these graphs that there are differences between the equilibrium points.

- In Case 1 none of the solution curves, apart from the lines $y = -x$ and $y = \frac{1}{4}x$, passes through the equilibrium point O. Further, unless the particle starts on the line $y = -x$ it never reaches O and indeed eventually moves further and further away from it.
- In Case 2 the solution curves circle round the equilibrium point, O, getting neither closer nor further away. The only 'curve' that reaches O is the point itself.
- In Case 3 all the curves converge on to the equilibrium point $(1, 2)$.

Systems, like these three, in which $\frac{dx}{dt}$ and $\frac{dy}{dt}$ are not dependent on t are called *autonomous*. For autonomous systems, equilibrium points may be found by setting $\frac{dx}{dt}$ and $\frac{dy}{dt}$ both equal to zero, as in the next example.

EXAMPLE 9.3

Find the equilibrium point for the system

$$\frac{dx}{dt} = 3x - 2y$$

$$\frac{dy}{dt} = x - 2y + 4.$$

SOLUTION

The equilibrium point is given by

$$3x - 2y = 0$$
$$x - 2y + 4 = 0. \qquad ②$$

Subtracting ② from ① gives

$$2x - 4 = 0$$
$$\Rightarrow \qquad x = 2.$$

Substituting this in either equation gives $y = 3$, so the equilibrium point of the system is $(2, 3)$.

Investigating the solution of a system by looking at its behaviour near an equilibrium point can provide a great deal of qualitative information without requiring detailed mathematical analysis. For a linear system, like the one in example 9.3, you can solve the equations analytically, then use a parametric plot facility to draw a range of solution curves. For most non-linear systems, though, you cannot solve the equations analytically.

INVESTIGATION

Equilibrium points

For a system with two dependent variables (e.g. x and y) there are six types of equilibrium points and these are the subject of the following investigation.

For each of the systems below
(i) identify the equilibrium point
(ii) draw the family of solution curves
(iii) describe the behaviour of the system near the equilibrium point.

(a) $\dfrac{dx}{dt} = 2x + y$

$\dfrac{dy}{dt} = x + 2y$

(b) $\dfrac{dx}{dt} = y$

$\dfrac{dy}{dt} = x$

(c) $\dfrac{dx}{dt} = x - y$

$\dfrac{dy}{dt} = x + y$

(d) $\dfrac{dx}{dt} = -y$

$\dfrac{dy}{dt} = x$

(e) $\dfrac{dx}{dt} = x + y$

$\dfrac{dy}{dt} = y$

(f) $\dfrac{dx}{dt} = x$

$\dfrac{dy}{dt} = y$

❺ Non-linear systems

So far in this chapter we have looked exclusively at linear systems. These have the advantage that the equations can be solved analytically. Unfortunately, though, many real systems are non-linear, and often they cannot be solved analytically. That does not mean that the preceding work is of no use.

For a start, you can use the expressions for $\dfrac{dx}{dt}$ and $\dfrac{dy}{dt}$ to find a single expression for $\dfrac{dy}{dx}$, and plot the tangent field.

EXAMPLE 9.4

You are given the non-linear system of differential equations

$$\frac{dx}{dt} = x - y^2$$

$$\frac{dy}{dt} = x^2 - y.$$

(i) Draw the tangent field for the relationship between y and x.

(ii) Draw a number of solution curves.

SOLUTION

(i) An expression for the gradients of the direction indicators may be found by using

$$\frac{dy}{dx} = \frac{\dfrac{dy}{dt}}{\dfrac{dx}{dt}} = \frac{x^2 - y}{x - y^2}.$$

This allows the value of $\dfrac{dy}{dx}$ to be calculated at any point. Figure 9.11 shows the tangent field.

Figure 9.11

(ii) Several solution curves are shown in figure 9.12.

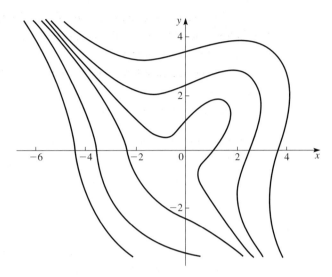

Figure 9.12

INVESTIGATION

These solution curves do not tell you what happens in the first quadrant near the origin. Investigate the behaviour of the curve there.

By investigating equilibrium points and using numerical methods akin to Euler's method (Chapter 5), it is often possible to investigate a non-linear system thoroughly. A spreadsheet package is very helpful in this.

The next example involves a non-linear predator–prey model.

EXAMPLE 9.5

A closed environment (such as a small island) supports populations of rabbits and foxes. At time t years their sizes are given by r and f. The rabbits feed off the vegetation and the foxes eat the rabbits.

A proposed model for this situation is given by the pair of differential equations

> This equation is non-linear because it contains a term in r^2.

$$\frac{dr}{dt} = k_1 r \left(1 - \frac{r}{r_m}\right) - \lambda f$$

$$\frac{df}{dt} = k_2 f \left(\alpha \frac{r}{f} - 1\right).$$

> This equation is linear.

The meanings of the various terms in this model are as follows:

- r_m is the greatest number of rabbits the environment can support
- α is the ratio of foxes to rabbits above which the number of foxes starts to decline due to starvation
- k_1, k_2 are constants related to the number of offspring per rabbit and fox respectively in one year
- λ is the number of rabbits eaten per fox in a year.

Following preliminary investigations, the values below are assigned to these parameters:

$$r_m = 12\,000 \qquad \alpha = 0.01$$
$$k_1 = 3 \qquad k_2 = 1$$
$$\lambda = 50.$$

(i) Substitute the assigned values into the differential equations and find the values of r and f at the equilibrium points.

(ii) Use a step-by-step method with steps of one year to estimate the populations for the next 25 years, given that their initial values are $r = 400$ and $f = 2$.

(iii) Draw graphs of r and f against t, and f against r.

SOLUTION

(i) Substituting the assigned parameter values gives

$$\frac{dr}{dt} = 3r\left(1 - \frac{1}{12\,000}r\right) - 50f \qquad \qquad ①$$

$$\frac{df}{dt} = 0.01r - f. \qquad \qquad ②$$

At an equilibrium point both $\dfrac{dr}{dt} = 0$ and $\dfrac{df}{dt} = 0$, so that (in equation ②)

$$0.01r - f = 0$$
$$\Rightarrow \qquad r = 100f.$$

Substituting for r in equation ① with $\dfrac{dr}{dt} = 0$ gives

$$300f\left(1 - \frac{f}{120}\right) - 50f = 0$$
$$\Rightarrow \qquad f^2 - 100f = 0$$
$$\Rightarrow \qquad f = 0 \text{ or } 100.$$

The corresponding values of r are $r = 0$ or $10\,000$.

There are two equilibrium points: $r = 0$, $f = 0$ and $r = 10\,000$, $f = 100$.

(ii) Using a spreadsheet gives value of r and f as shown below.

time	rabbits	foxes	time	rabbits	foxes
0	400	2	13	7522.4973	118.000 25
1	1460	4	14	10049.923	75.524 973
2	5107.1	14.6	15	11173.206	100.499 23
3	13177.782	51.071	16	8457.7303	111.732 06
4	6744.0924	131.777 82	17	10361.018	84.577 303
5	9016.7828	67.440 924	18	10377.533	103.610 18
6	12369.492	90.167 828	19	9406.3247	103.775 33
7	6718.4935	123.694 92	20	10316.796	94.063 247
8	9404.6893	67.184 935	21	9954.9517	103.167 96
9	12147.465	94.046 893	22	9886.1429	99.549 517
10	6997.2884	121.474 65	23	10133.14	98.861 429
11	9674.9097	69.972 884	24	9919.3566	101.3314
12	11800.025	96.749 097	25	10012.447	99.193 566

(iii) These results are illustrated in figures 9.13 and 9.14.

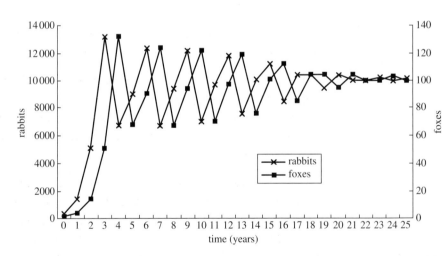

Figure 9.13 *Graph showing the sizes of the rabbit and fox populations with time (notice the different vertical scales).*

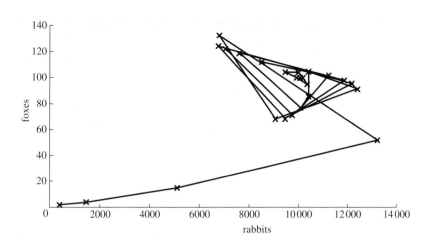

Figure 9.14 *Solution 'curve' showing the variation of the number of foxes with the number of rabbits.*

This example illustrates several important points.

- Even though you cannot solve the non-linear system analytically you are able to investigate the system using familiar methods.
- You can use step-by-step methods to investigate the behaviour of non-linear systems.
- Using a spreadsheet means you can investigate the system with different initial conditions. It is also easy to see what happens if you change the values of the assigned parameters.

If you try different initial conditions in this example (with the assigned parameters), you will find that one of three patterns emerges:

- convergence to the non-zero equilibrium point as in the case above: this corresponds to stable populations
- convergence to the zero equilibrium point: the populations die out
- a three-year cycle between certain pairs of values of r and f, none of which is an equilibrium point.

Population cycles occur naturally; the best known is a ten-year cycle exhibited by many Arctic mammals in Canada and Siberia (and also Scotland). Data collected by the Hudson Bay Company on fur sales go back over 250 years and show this cycle for, among other species, the Canadian Lynx and the Arctic Hare. Other animals are found to follow a four-year cycle. The model in this example is a simple one involving only two species; real food chains are usually more complicated.

It would seem that the accuracy could be improved by taking shorter step lengths. Given the breeding patterns of rabbits and foxes, investigate whether doing so would improve the solution.

Investigate the effect of changing the parameters in the rabbit and fox example.

State why it is important to be able to construct mathematical models of animal populations.

Historical note

The study of non-linear systems of differential equations has only just begun. Until the invention of computers, the standard method of dealing with a non-linear system was to try to transform it into a linear one; if this could not be done, there was little more that could be achieved. The application of computers to non-linear systems has opened up a whole new area of mathematics often known as *chaos*. Many of their solutions show instability: a small change in the initial conditions produces a large change in the solution, a phenomenon known as the *butterfly effect*. However, there are found to be patterns of order within such instability and these can often be represented by beautiful fractal diagrams.

EXERCISE 9A

1 For each of the following systems of equations:
 (a) solve the equations to find expressions for x and y in terms of t
 (b) find the particular solutions for which $x = 1$ and $y = 2$ at $t = 0$
 (c) describe the long-term behaviour of the system.

 (i) $\dfrac{dx}{dt} = 3x - y$
 $\dfrac{dy}{dt} = 2x$

 (ii) $\dfrac{dx}{dt} = x + y$
 $\dfrac{dy}{dt} = x - y$

 (iii) $\dfrac{dx}{dt} = x + 2y - 3$
 $\dfrac{dy}{dt} = -3x + y + 2$

 (iv) $\dfrac{dx}{dt} = 2x + 3y$
 $\dfrac{dy}{dt} = 3x + 2y$

 (v) $\dfrac{dx}{dt} = x + 5y$
 $\dfrac{dy}{dt} = -x - 3y$

 (vi) $\dfrac{dx}{dt} = 2x - y - 1$
 $\dfrac{dy}{dt} = 2y - 6$

2 A population of cells consisting of a mixture of two-chromosome and four-chromosome cells is described approximately by the equations

$$\dfrac{dT}{dt} = (a - b)T, \qquad \dfrac{dF}{dt} = bT + cF$$

where T is the number of two-chromosome cells and F is the number of four-chromosome cells. The variables T and F clearly cannot be negative, and a, b and c are constants with $a \neq b$ and $c \neq 0$.

Show that whatever the values of a, b and c, the proportion of two-chromosome cells in the population tends to a constant value in the long term, independent of the initial conditions.

Find conditions on the values of a, b and c which ensure that this limiting value of the proportion is non-zero, and find an expression for the limit when this is the case.

3 In a chemical decomposition a compound X produces a compound Y which in turn gives a compound Z. These decompositions are governed by the system of differential equations

$$\frac{dx}{dt} = -4x, \quad \frac{dy}{dt} = 4x - 2y, \quad \frac{dz}{dt} = 2y$$

where x, y and z are the masses in grams of X, Y and Z respectively, and time t is measured in hours.

Initially $x = 8$, $y = 0$ and $z = 0$.
(i) Find x, y and z in terms of t.
(ii) Determine the maximum value of y.
(iii) Determine the final value of z.

4 In a radioactive decomposition 1 gram of an unstable isotope X decays into an unstable isotope Y which in turn decays into a stable isotope Z. Assuming the loss of mass in each decomposition is negligible, the decomposition process may be modelled by the three simultaneous differential equations

$$\frac{dx}{dt} = -0.5x, \quad \frac{dy}{dt} = 0.5x - 0.3y, \quad \frac{dz}{dt} = 0.3y$$

where x, y and z are the masses of X, Y and Z respectively at time t.
(i) Solve the first differential equation to find x as a function of time.
(ii) Use the result of part (i) in the second differential equation to find y as a function of time.

(iii) Use the results of parts (i) and (ii) to deduce z as a function of time.
(iv) Briefly describe how the masses of X, Y and Z vary with time.

[MEI]

5 In a predator–prey environment the rate of growth of the predator population is found to be proportional to the size of the prey population. The rate of change of the prey population, however, is found to depend upon the sizes of both the predator and prey populations. The population dynamics are modelled by assuming that both populations vary continuously. The differential equations governing the relationships between the two populations are

$$100\frac{dx}{dt} = y \text{ and } 100\frac{dy}{dt} = 2y - x$$

where x and y are the numbers of predator and prey respectively and t is the time in years.

Initially the predator population is 10 thousand and the prey population 5 million.

(i) By eliminating y between the two equations show that the predator population, x, satisfies the second order differential equation

$$10\,000\frac{d^2x}{dt^2} - 200\frac{dx}{dt} + x = 0.$$

(ii) Solve this equation to find the predator population as a function of time.
(iii) Find the prey population, y, as a function of time.
(iv) Determine the size of each population after five years.

[MEI]

6 For a series of experiments a tank is split into two compartments by a semi-permeable membrane. The first compartment has a volume of V_1 litres and is filled with a solution of a chemical with a concentration of C_1 moles per litre. The second compartment has a volume of V_2 litres and is filled with a solution of the same chemical but with a concentration of C_2 moles per litre. The chemical diffuses

through the membrane at a rate proportional to the difference in concentration between the two solutions and in a direction such as to equalise the two concentrations. The differential equations modelling the diffusion process are

$$\frac{dC_1}{dt} = -\frac{k}{V_1}(C_1 - C_2)$$

$$\frac{dC_2}{dt} = \frac{k}{V_2}(C_1 - C_2)$$

where t is the time in hours and k is a constant of diffusion measured in litres per hour.

In a particular experiment $V_1 = 20$, $V_2 = 5$, $k = 0.2$ and, initially, $C_1 = 3$ and $C_2 = 0$.

(i) By eliminating C_2 between the two equations show that C_1 satisfies the second order differential equation

$$\frac{d^2C_1}{dt^2} + 0.05\frac{dC_1}{dt} = 0.$$

(ii) Solve this equation to find C_1 as a function of time.

(iii) Find C_2 as a function of time.

(iv) Determine both concentrations after four hours, and their final values.

[MEI]

7 The numbers of combatants in each of two armies are denoted, in thousands, by x and y. Each army is reinforced at a rate proportional to its number of combatants and suffers casualties at a rate proportional to the number of combatants in the opposing army. In addition the conflict takes place in a hostile environment which reduces the number of combatants in each army at a constant rate. The pair of simultaneous differential equations modelling the numbers in the conflicting armies are

$$\dot{x} = x - y - 3$$
$$\text{and} \quad \dot{y} = y - 4x - 3,$$

where initially $x = 4$, $y = 6$ and t is the time in years.

(i) Write down the initial values of $\dot{x}$ and $\dot{y}$.

(ii) By differentiating the first equation with respect to time and then eliminating $\dot{y}$ from it by using the second equation, show that x satisfies $\ddot{x} - 2\dot{x} - 3x = 6$.

(iii) Find x as a function of t.

(iv) Hence find y as a function of t.

[MEI]

8 The following pair of differential equations provides a simple model for the absorption of a drug by the blood and body tissue. Units are μg and days.

$$\frac{dx}{dt} = -0.05x + 0.01y + 25$$

$$\frac{dy}{dt} = 0.01x - 0.03y$$

where x and y are the amounts of the drug in the blood and the body tissue at time t.

(i) By eliminating y between the two equations, show that x satisfies the second order differential equation

$$\frac{d^2x}{dt^2} + 0.08\frac{dx}{dt} + 0.0014x = 0.75.$$

(ii) Solve the equation to find the general solution for x in terms of t.

(iii) Find the general solution for y in terms of t.

Initially $x = 0$ and $y = 0$.

(iv) Find the particular solutions for x and y in terms of t, and sketch graphs of x and y against t.

(v) Find the equilibrium levels of the drug in the blood and body tissue.

9 Each of two competing species of insect reproduces at a rate proportional to its own number and is adversely affected by the other species at a rate proportional to the number of that other species. At time t, measured in centuries, the populations of these two species are x million and y million. The situation is modelled by the pair of simultaneous equations

$$\frac{dx}{dt} = 2x - 3y \quad \text{and} \quad \frac{dy}{dt} = y - 2x$$

where, initially, at time $t = 0$, $x = 15$ and $y = 10$.

(i)   Find the initial rates of change of both x and y.

(ii) Differentiate the first differential equation with respect to t and use this together with the two original differential equations to eliminate y and obtain a second order differential equation for x.

(iii) Solve this second order equation to find x as a function of t.

(iv) Hence find y as a function of t.

(v)   Show that one of the species becomes extinct and determine the time at which this occurs.

[MEI]

10 A radioactive substance P decays and changes (without loss of mass) into a substance Q, which itself similarly changes into a third substance R. R suffers no further change. The masses of P, Q and R present at time t are given by p, q and r grams respectively. The rates of change are such that

$$\frac{dp}{dt} = -2p \qquad \qquad ①$$

and $\dfrac{dr}{dt} = q.$

Show that $\dfrac{dq}{dt} = 2p - q.$

Initially (at time $t = 0$) there is 1 g of substance P and none of substance Q. Integrate equation ① and hence show that q satisfies the differential equation

$$\frac{dq}{dt} + q = 2e^{-2t}. \qquad \qquad ②$$

Show that ② may be written in the form

$$\frac{d}{dt}(qe^t) = 2e^{-t}$$

and integrate to find q as a function of t. Hence prove that, at any subsequent time, there is never more than $\frac{1}{2}$ g of Q present.

[SMP]

11 A solution contains substances A, B and C. A chemical reaction changes substance B into substance C at a rate kp where p is the mass of substance C present at time t and k is a constant; simultaneously, a second reaction changes substance A into substance B at a rate of $2kq$, where q is the *combined* mass of substances B and C present.

Write down equations for $\dfrac{dp}{dt}$ and $\dfrac{dq}{dt}$.

Initially 48 g of A, 1 g of B and 1 g of C are present. By solving your equations, show that substance A is exhausted at time t_1, where $kt_1 = \ln 5$, and that the two reactions are completed at time t_2, where $kt_2 = \ln 50$. Find the maximum amount of substance B present during the reaction.

[SMP]

12 The value of the assets of a company at time t years after it was founded is £V. The rate of increase of annual profits £P is a positive constant fraction α of the value of the assets of the company,

$$\frac{dP}{dt} = \alpha V.$$

A constant fraction $k^2\alpha$ of the annual profits £P are reinvested in the company and this gives the rate of increase in the value of the assets,

$$\frac{dV}{dt} = k^2\alpha P.$$

The remaining profits are distributed as dividends to shareholders.

Given that initially the assets of the company are V_0 and its annual profits are P_0,

(i)   write down the initial value of $\dfrac{dV}{dt}$

(ii) derive a differential equation for V in terms of t

(iii) find the general solution of the differential equation for V, and hence show that

$$V = \tfrac{1}{2}(V_0 + kP_0)e^{k\alpha t} + \tfrac{1}{2}(V_0 - kP_0)e^{-k\alpha t}$$

(iv) determine P as a function of t.

(v) Given that $\alpha = \frac{1}{8}$, $k = 2$ and $P_0 = \frac{1}{10} V_0$, determine the time it takes for the profits to increase by a factor of 10.

[MEI]

13 In a chemical process, compound P reacts with an abundant supply of a gas to form compound Q. The process is governed by two reaction rates, one for the forward reaction, and a lesser one for the reverse reaction, where Q decomposes into P and the gas. P is introduced into a reaction chamber at a constant rate of 21 kg per hour and Q is extracted at a rate proportional to the quantity of Q in the chamber. The equations which describe the process are

$$\frac{dp}{dt} = -5p + q + 21$$

$$\frac{dq}{dt} = -8q + 10p,$$

where p and q are the quantities (in kg) of P and Q respectively and t is the time in hours.

(i) Calculate the values of p and q for which $\frac{dp}{dt}$ and $\frac{dq}{dt}$ are both zero.

(ii) Eliminate q to show that
$$\frac{d^2p}{dt^2} + 13\frac{dp}{dt} + 30p = 168.$$

(iii) Find the general solution of the differential equation in part (ii). Hence find the particular solutions for p and q for which $p = q = 0$ when $t = 0$.

(iv) Sketch the graphs of the solutions, showing the significance of your answers to part (i).

[MEI]

14 To control the population of rabbits, foxes are introduced on to an island. As long as $r \geqslant 0$ and $f \geqslant 0$, the populations are modelled by the equations

$$50\frac{df}{dt} = r \quad \text{and} \quad \frac{dr}{dt} = r - 8f$$

where f is the fox population and r is the rabbit population at time t years after the foxes are introduced.

(i) Eliminate f from the equations to show that r satisfies $25\frac{d^2r}{dt^2} - 25\frac{dr}{dt} + 4r = 0$.

(ii) Solve this equation to find the general solution for r.

Initially the rabbit population is 12 000 and the fox population is denoted by f_0.

(iii) Find the solutions for f and r subject to these conditions.

(iv) Show that for $f_0 > 1200$ the rabbit population will die out.

(v) Is it possible for the fox population to die out before the rabbit population? Explain your answer.

[MEI]

15 Water is leaking from a small hole in the base of a tank. The water is collecting on the floor and, as a temporary measure, a pump is used to remove the water from the floor. The rate of flow of water from the tank is modelled as being proportional to the depth of the water in the tank. While the depth of the water on the floor is less than 3 cm, the rate at which the pump removes water is modelled as being proportional to the depth of water on the floor. The system can be described by the equations

$$\frac{dx}{dt} = -2x \quad \text{and} \quad \frac{dy}{dt} = \frac{x}{10} - ay \text{ for } y < 3$$

where x is the depth of water (in cm) in the tank, y is the depth of water (in cm) on the floor and a is a positive constant which depends on the type of pump used. The time t is measured in hours. When $t = 0$, $x = 100$ and $y = 0$.

(i) Solve the first equation to express x in terms of t.

(ii) Hence given $a \neq 2$ solve the second equation to show that
$$y = \frac{10}{a-2}(e^{-2t} - e^{-at}).$$

(iii) If $a = 1$, show that the maximum value of y is less than 3.

For the pump being used $a = 0.5$

(iv) Verify that at $t = 0.65$, $y \approx 3$.

When the depth of water on the floor is 3 cm or greater, the inlet valve of the pump is fully submerged and the rate at which the pump removes water is constant. The second equation then becomes $\dfrac{dy}{dt} = \dfrac{x}{10} - 1.5$

(v) Use your solution for x (which is still valid) and the values for a and t given in part (iv) to solve this equation to find an expression for y in terms of t while $y \geqslant 3$. Calculate the maximum value of y.

[**MEI**]

16 A radioactive element X decays into element Y, which in turn decays into the stable element Z. The equations modelling the decay are

$$\frac{dx}{dt} = -2x \;①, \quad \frac{dy}{dt} = 2x - 4y \;②, \quad \frac{dz}{dt} = 4y \;③$$

where x, y and z are the masses in grams of elements X, Y and Z respectively, and t is the time in hours. Initially there are 5 g of X and there is no Y or Z.

(i) Solve equation ① to find x in terms of t.

(ii) Hence solve equation ② to find y in terms of t.

(iii) Find the maximum value of y. What is the limiting value of y after a long period of time?

Illustrate these answers on a sketch graph of y against t.

(iv) Without solving for z, use the differential equations to show that $x + y + z = 5$. Interpret this in physical terms.

(v) Hence, or otherwise, write down the solution for z and sketch its graph.

[**MEI**]

17 A fish in a polluted lake absorbs a chemical into its bloodstream and body tissue. The amounts of chemical are modelled by the equations

$$\frac{dx}{dt} = k - 0.04x + 0.01y \qquad\qquad ①$$

$$\frac{dy}{dt} = 0.03x - 0.02y. \qquad\qquad ②$$

In these equations, x is the amount, in micrograms, of chemical in the blood, y is the amount, in micrograms, of chemical in the body tissue, t is the time in days and k is a constant which depends on the level of pollution in the lake.

(i) Eliminate y from the equations to show that

$$2000\frac{d^2x}{dt^2} + 120\frac{dx}{dt} + x = 40k.$$

A fish is placed into a lake for which $k = 5$. The initial values of x and y are both zero.

(ii) Solve the differential equation in part (i) to find x in terms of t.

Hence show that

$$y = 300 - 375e^{-0.01t} + 75e^{-0.05t}.$$

At some subsequent time, the (now polluted) fish is removed and placed in a clean lake for which $k = 0$. The time is now recorded from this point.

(iii) By comparing with your work in part (ii), write down the general solution for x in terms of t. Use equation ① to find the corresponding general solution for y in terms of t.

Does the fish ever completely clear the pollution from both its bloodstream and body tissue? Explain your reasoning.

[**MEI**]

18 The differential equation

$$\frac{dx}{dt} = 2x - 10y, \qquad\qquad ①$$

$$\frac{dy}{dt} = 5x - 12y, \qquad\qquad ②$$

are to be solved simultaneously.

(i) Elimate y from the equations to show that

$$\frac{d^2x}{dt^2} + 10\frac{dx}{dt} + 26x = 0.$$

(ii) Find the general solution for x in terms of t. Hence use this solution and equation ① to find the general solution for y in terms of t.

The differential equations

$$\frac{dx}{dt} = 2x - 10y + 26, \qquad ③$$

$$\frac{dy}{dt} = 5x - 12y + 13, \qquad ④$$

are to be solved simultaneously.

(iii) Verify that the constant solution $x = 7$, $y = 4$ is a particular solution of equations ③ and ④.

Let the solutions found in part (ii) be $x = f(t)$, $y = g(t)$.

(iv) Verify that $x = f(t) + 7$, $y = g(t) + 4$ satisfy equations ③ and ④.

[MEI]

19 A radioactive element X decays into the radioactive element Y which decays into the stable element Z. The decay can be modelled by the differential equations

$$\frac{dx}{dt} = -0.1x, \qquad ①$$

$$\frac{dy}{dt} = 0.1x - 0.2y, \qquad ②$$

$$\frac{dz}{dt} = 0.2y, \qquad ③$$

where x, y and z are the masses (in milligrams) of X, Y and Z respectively at time t seconds.

When $t = 0$, the mass of X is 25 mg, and there is no Y or Z present.

(i) Solve equation ① to find x in terms of t. Sketch a graph of your solution.
(ii) Use your solution for x to solve equation ② to find y in terms of t.
(iii) Calculate the range of times for which the amount of Y is increasing. Sketch a graph of the mass of Y against time, showing the maximum value.
(iv) Without solving equation ③, show that $x + y + z$ is constant. Hence find z in terms of t, and verify that this satisfies equation ③ and the initial conditions.

[MEI]

20 The size, w, of a rabbit population at time t years on an island with a plentiful food supply is modelled, in the absence of predators, by the differential equation

$$\frac{dw}{dt} = 2w,$$

with $w = 2000$ when $t = 0$.

(i) Solve the differential equation to find w in terms of t. Describe the behaviour of the solution and say whether this is likely to describe the actual situation.

Foxes are introduced to the island. The foxes kill rabbits, but also compete with each other if the rabbit population is too small. The size of the fox population at time t years is x. The situation is now modelled by the equations

$$\frac{dw}{dt} = 2w - 80x,$$

$$\frac{dx}{dt} = 0.2x\left(1 - \frac{100x}{w}\right),$$

with $w = 2000$ and $x = 25$ when $t = 0$.

(ii) Without solving the equations, find the range of values of $\frac{w}{x}$, (i.e. the ratio of rabbits to foxes) for which
(a) the rabbit population increases
(b) the fox population increases
(c) the rabbit population increases while the fox population decreases.

A numerical solution to the equations is sought using a step-by-step method. The algorithm is given by

$$t_{r+1} = t_r + h,$$
$$w_{r+1} = w_r + hf(w_r, x_r),$$
$$x_{r+1} = x_r + hg(w_r, x_r)$$

where $f(w, x) = \dfrac{dw}{dt}$ and $g(w, x) = \dfrac{dx}{dt}$.

The table shows the initial values and the results of the first iteration.

t	w	x
0	2000	25
0.1	2200	24.875
0.2		

(iii) Verify the entries for $t = 0.1$ and calculate the entries for $t = 0.2$

(iv) Explain briefly why the calculated values of x *cannot* be the actual numbers of foxes at these times. What aspect of the model has led to this inaccuracy?

[MEI]

21 A chemical reaction takes place in a chamber. Compound X is injected into the chamber at a constant rate and compound Y (which is produced in the reaction) is extracted at a rate proportional to the quantity of compound Y in the chamber. The equations modelling the system are

$$\frac{dx}{dt} = -4x + y + 28,$$

$$\frac{dy}{dt} = 6x - 5y,$$

where x grams and y grams are the quantities in the chamber of compounds X and Y respectively, and t is the time in minutes.

(i) Eliminate y from the equations to show that

$$\frac{d^2x}{dt^2} + 9\frac{dx}{dt} + 14x = 140.$$

Initially there is no X and there is no Y in the chamber.

(ii) Solve the differential equation to find x in terms of t. Hence find y in terms of t.

(iii) Sketch a graph of the solutions, indicating the values of x and y after a long period of time.

Explain clearly how, if it is known that such long-term values exist, they can be calculated without finding the solutions for x and y in terms of t.

[MEI]

22 The solution is sought for the equations

$$\frac{dx}{dt} = 4x - y + 50\sin t$$

$$\frac{dy}{dt} = 6x - 3y + 50\cos t.$$

(i) Eliminate y from the equations to show that

$$\frac{d^2x}{dt^2} - \frac{dx}{dt} - 6x = 150\sin t.$$

(ii) Find the general solution for x in terms of t.

It is given that when $t = 0$, $x = 0$ and $y = 15$.

(iii) Find the particular solutions for x and y in terms of t.

[MEI]

23 Two reservoirs, A and B, are connected by a river. Water flows from A to B at a rate proportional to the volume of water in A. After heavy rainfall, water also flows into each reservoir from the surrounding land at an exponentially decaying rate. The equations modelling the situation are

$$\frac{dx}{dt} = 10e^{-6t} - x, \qquad \qquad ①$$

$$\frac{dy}{dt} = 8e^{-6t} + x, \qquad \qquad ②$$

where x km^3 is the volume of water in reservoir A, y km^3 is the volume of water in reservoir B and t is the time in days.

When $t = 0$, $x = 5$ and $y = 4$.

(i) Solve equation ① to show that
$x = 7e^{-t} - 2e^{-6t}$.

(ii) Hence solve equation ② to find y in terms of t.

(iii) Determine whether x is increasing or decreasing initially. Sketch the graphs of x and y against t.

(iv) Find the maximum rate of decrease of the volume of water in reservoir A.

[MEI]

24 The following pair of differential equations is proposed as an economic model for the price P of a single item in a market where Q is the number of the item available:

$$\frac{dP}{dt} = aP\left(\frac{b}{Q} - P\right)$$

$$\frac{dQ}{dt} = cQ(fP - Q)$$

where a, b, c and f are positive constants.

Consider the case $a = 1$, $b = 20\,000$, $c = 1$ and $f = 30$. Find the equilibrium points for this economic model.

25 The following pair of differential equations is a simple predator–prey model for the population of foxes and rabbits in a park in Reading.

$$\frac{dR}{dt} = R(120 - 0.1R - 2F)$$

$$\frac{dF}{dt} = F(80 - 0.1R + 2F).$$

Find the equilibrium populations of foxes and rabbits.

26 Two large tanks on a chemical plant, connected by a series of pipes as in the diagram, each hold 100 litres of water.

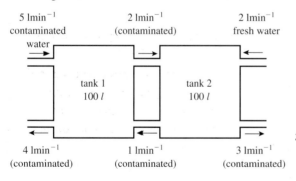

| 5 lmin^{-1} contaminated water | 2 lmin^{-1} (contaminated) | 2 lmin^{-1} fresh water |

| 4 lmin^{-1} (contaminated) | 1 lmin^{-1} (contaminated) | 3 lmin^{-1} (contaminated) |

Contaminated water containing 2 kgl^{-1} of a chemical enters tank 1 at a rate of 5 l min^{-1}. The flow rates of water along the pipes into and out of each tank are shown in the figure. Fresh water also flows into tank 2 at a rate of 2 l min^{-1}. The liquid in each tank is continuously stirred to ensure uniform concentration of chemical in each tank. Initially the whole system contained fresh water only.

(i) Show that the following pair of differential equations models the amount of chemical in each tank at any time.

$$\frac{dx}{dt} = 10 - 0.06x + 0.01y$$

$$\frac{dy}{dt} = 0.02x - 0.04y$$

where x and y kg are the quantities of the chemical in tanks 1 and 2 respectively at time t minutes.

(ii) Find the equilibrium levels of the chemical in each tank.

(iii) The graph shows the direction field for the differential equation

$$\frac{dy}{dx} = \frac{0.02x - 0.04y}{10 - 0.06x + 0.01y}.$$

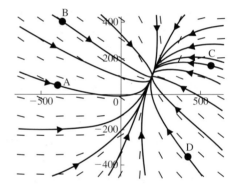

Describe what happens to the amount of the chemical in each tank if at some instant the values of x and y correspond to the co-ordinates of point A. Repeat this for points B, C and D.

27 The map below shows three interconnected lakes. The data for each lake is shown in the table overleaf.

Characteristic	Lake A	Lake B	Lake C
Volume of water (km³)	4871	458	1636
Average outflow rate (km³ per year)	209	175	209
Input of chemical pollution (kg per year)	50 000		

A river bearing polluted water flows into Lake A. Water flows directly from Lake A into Lakes B and C and directly from Lake B into Lake C. Water flows from Lake C into the river. Assume that perfect mixing occurs and that the volume of water in each lake remains constant.

(i)   Set up a mathematical model for the flow of pollution through the three lakes and find the equilibrium pollution levels in kgl⁻¹, giving your answers to 2 significant figures.

(ii) Starting from an initial pollution-free state, find how long it takes Lake A to reach half of its final pollution level.

(iii) At a time when all the lakes have reached their equilibrium pollution levels, the source of pollution is removed. How long does it take for the pollution in Lake A to reach half its original level?

e *The remaining questions relate to enrichment material.*

28 **(i)** Find the equilibrium points of the following systems:

   (a) $\dfrac{dx}{dt} = 2x - 3$

$$\dfrac{dy}{dt} = x + y + 1$$

   (b) $\dfrac{dx}{dt} = x - y + 2$

$$\dfrac{dy}{dt} = 3x + y + 2$$

   (c) $\dfrac{dx}{dt} = x(x - y)$

$$\dfrac{dy}{dt} = y^2 + 3x + 2$$

(Notice that part (c) is an example of a non-linear system.)

(iii) Suppose that (x_f, y_f) is the equilibrium point of the linear system

$$\dfrac{dx}{dt} = a_1x + b_1y + c_1$$

$$\dfrac{dy}{dt} = a_2x + b_2y + c_2.$$

   (a) Show that the change of variables $X = x - x_f$, $Y = y - y_f$ simplifies the system to

$$\dfrac{dX}{dt} = a_1X + b_1Y$$

$$\dfrac{dY}{dt} = a_2X + b_2Y$$

   whose equilibrium point is the origin $(0, 0)$.

   (b) Hence show that any autonomous linear system involving two dependent variables can be reduced to a homogeneous linear second order differential equation with constant coefficients in one of the variables.

9

A cascade of water tanks

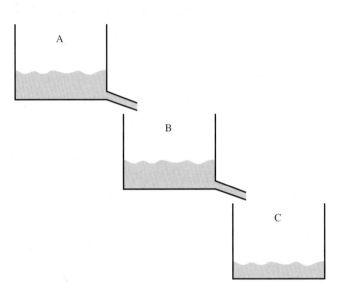

Figure 9.15

Figure 9.15 shows three tanks. Initially tank A is full of water and tanks B and C are empty. In the final state tanks A and B are empty and tank C is full.

The amount of water in tank B varies between the start and the finish. Construct a mathematical model to predict when tank B will contain its maximum volume, and what that maximum volume will be.

Note

Before you construct your model you will need to find out, either by experiments or other research, the relationship between the flow rate out of a tank and the depth of water in it.

KEY POINTS

1 A system of differential equations involves two or more dependent variables and one independent variable.

2 In a linear system

$$\frac{dx}{dt} = a_1 x + b_1 y + f_1(t) \quad \text{①}$$

$$\frac{dy}{dt} = a_2 x + b_2 y + f_2(t) \quad \text{②}$$

x and y are the dependent variables, and t the independent variable.

3 Solving such a system of equations involves finding x in terms of t and y in terms of t.

4 The relationship between x and t may be found by:

(i) differentiating equation ①

(ii) substituting for $\dfrac{dy}{dt}$ from equation ② and for y from equation ①

(iii) solving the resulting second order linear differential equation.

The relationship between y and t may then be found by substituting for $\dfrac{dx}{dt}$ and x in equation ①.

5 In the case when $f_1(t) = 0$ and $f_2(t) = 0$ the resulting second order linear differential equation is homogeneous; otherwise it is non-homogeneous.

6 The graph of y against x is called the solution curve.

7 If the solution reaches an equilibrium point it does not move away from it. It may alternatively approach an equilibrium point as $t \to \infty$.

e Non-linear systems may be investigated by:

(i) drawing the tangent field

(ii) investigating equilibrium points

(iii) using a step-by-step method of solution.

Answers

Chapter 1

❓ (Page 5)

1 The greater the temperature difference between the coffee and the room, the faster the coffee cools, slowing down as the coffee temperature approaches that of the room.

2 In theory human population increases at a rate proportional to the present population. Other factors are involved, however, for example, population movement, emigration, epidemics, natural disasters, famine, birth control.

3 It decreases initially at a rate proportional to the pollution present. It can be reduced to a specified safe level but never completely eradicated. In addition, there may be pockets of unacceptable pollution levels since perfect mixing is not possible.

Exercise 1A (Page 10)

1 $\dfrac{dm}{dt} = -km$

2 $\dfrac{dv}{dt} = -\dfrac{v^2}{400}$

3 $\dfrac{dP}{dt} = \dfrac{P}{34}$

4 $\dfrac{dP}{dt} = \dfrac{P}{6}$

5 $\dfrac{dV}{dt} = -2\sqrt{h}$

6 $\dfrac{dN}{dt} = 2\sqrt{N}$

7 $\dfrac{dC}{dt} = -0.2C$

8 $\dfrac{d\theta}{dt} = \dfrac{20 - \theta}{120}$

9 (i) $\dfrac{dA}{dt} = kr$

(ii) $\dfrac{dA}{dr} = 2\pi r$

(iii) $\dfrac{dr}{dt} = \dfrac{k}{2\pi}$

10 $\dfrac{dr}{dt} = -\dfrac{1}{100\pi}$

11 $\dfrac{d\theta}{dx} = -\dfrac{16}{25}x$

12 $\dfrac{dp}{dh} = \begin{cases} 9800(1 + 0.001h) & 0 \leqslant h \leqslant 100 \\ 10780 & h > 100 \end{cases}$

13 $\dfrac{dy}{dx} = \dfrac{b - y}{a + vt - x}$

14 $\dfrac{dh}{dt} = \dfrac{4.8}{\pi h^2}$

15 $\dfrac{dV}{dt} = -\sqrt{20h}, \ \dfrac{dh}{dt} = -\dfrac{\sqrt{5h}}{2}$

16 $\dfrac{d\theta}{dt} = k(22 - \theta)$

Exercise 1B (Page 16)

3 (ii) 0

(iii) Tends to 20

4 (iii) Coffee $T = 20 + 60e^{-0.1t}$

Juice $T = 20 - 18e^{-0.1t}$

5 (ii) $P = 50e^{\frac{t}{20}}$

(iii) $P = 100e^{\frac{t}{20}}$

(iv)

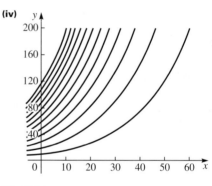

6 (ii) 69.3 hours

(iii) 20 mg

(iv) $m = 50e^{\frac{-t}{100}}$

8 $y = x^3 - \dfrac{x^2}{2} + x + 2.5$

9 $s = 4t - 5t^2 + c$

$s = 4t - 5t^2 + 11$

10 A and E

11 (iii) $A = P_0 e^{-kt_0}$

12 (ii) $a + A, a$

(iii) $a = 25, A = 65$

(iv)

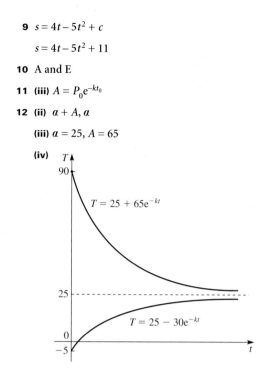

13 (ii) 4

Chapter 2

Exercise 2A (Page 24)

1 (i)

y \ x	−2	−1	0	1	2
2	−4	−2	0	2	4
1	−4	−2	0	2	4
0	−4	−2	0	2	4
−1	−4	−2	0	2	4
−2	−4	−2	0	2	4

(ii), (iii)

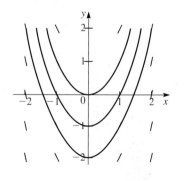

(iv) $y = x^2 + c$

(v) $y = x^2 - 2, y = x^2 - 1, y = x^2$.

(vi) The isoclines are straight lines parallel to the y axis.

2 (i)

y \ x	−2	−1	0	1	2
2	1.5	1	0.5	0	−0.5
1	3	2	1	0	−1
0	∞	∞	∞	—	∞
−1	−3	−2	−1	0	1
−2	−1.5	−1	−0.5	0	0.5

(ii), (iii)

(iv) $y = 2 - 2x$

(v) The isoclines are straight lines through the point $(1, 0)$ which is the common centre of the family of circles.

3 (i) The isoclines are straight lines parallel to the x axis

(ii), (iii)

4 (i) The isoclines are straight lines parallel to the x axis, $y = 1$.

(ii), (iii)

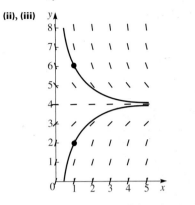

(iv) Each is the reflection of the other in the line $y = 4$.

5 (i), (ii)

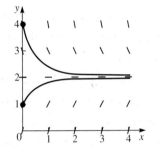

6 (i) See below

(ii) $y = mx$

(iii) **(c)** the y axis

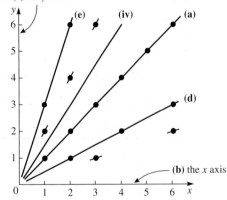

(iv) All straight lines coming from the origin.

(v) Gradient $= \frac{0}{0}$ which is undefined.

7 (i) $y = m - x$

(ii), (iii), (iv)

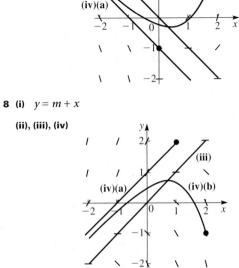

8 (i) $y = m + x$

(ii), (iii), (iv)

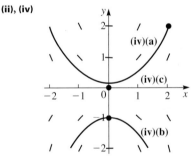

9 (i) $y = \frac{m}{x}$, rectangular hyperbola

(ii), (iv)

(iii) $xy = 0$ i.e. the x and y axes

10 (i), (ii)

(iii) $i = 3$

11 (i)

(ii) Terminal speed is $8\,\text{ms}^{-1}$.

12 (i), (ii), (iii)

(iv) $y = \frac{1}{2}e^{x^2/2}$

13 (i) $y = 0,\ y' = -1$,

$x = 0,\ y' = 3$

(ii) $y' = 0$ when $y = \frac{x}{3}$

$y' = \infty$ when $y = -x$

(iii) $m = 1$

(iv), (v)

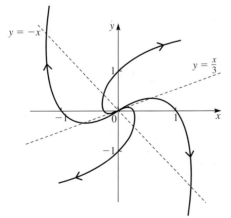

14 (ii) $u = 2x$

(iii) $x = 0,\ u' = 1$

$u = 0,\ u' = \pm\infty$

(iv)

(v) When $u > 0 \Rightarrow \dfrac{\mathrm{d}x}{\mathrm{d}t} < 0$ and so x decreases until $x = 0$ and the particle reaches the filter with finite speed.

When $u < 0 \Rightarrow \dfrac{\mathrm{d}x}{\mathrm{d}t} > 0$ and so x increases with t but, as the curves in part (iv) show, as x increases for negative u so $|u|$ decreases until it reaches the value $u = 0$ (and thus its maximum value of x). Then x decreases until the particle reaches $x = 0$ (the filter) with finite speed.

15 (i) (a) $y = \pm 2$

(b) $y = 0$

(iii)

x				
y				
-1.2	-0.7	-0.6	-0.5	-0.4
-3.0	-1.9	-1.5	-1.3	-1.1
-7.5	-4.7	-3.8	-3.2	-2.8

(iii) and (iv)

Chapter 2 side text.

(v) $y = -2$

(vi) x increases until the curve reaches the x axis then decreases until $(0, -k)$. It stops because $\dfrac{dy}{dx}$ does not exist for $x < 0$.

Chapter 3

❓ (Page 28)

No; no; yes, e.g. for $k = 1$, $n = -2$.

Exercise 3A (Page 34)

1 (i) $y = Ae^x$

(ii) $y = Ae^{\frac{1}{2}x^2}$

(iii) $y = Ae^{\frac{1}{4}x^4}$

(iv) $y = \ln(x^3 + c)$

(v) $\ln|1 + y| = \dfrac{x^2}{2} + c$ or $y = Ae^{\frac{1}{2}x^2} - 1$

(vi) not possible

(vii) $e^x + e^{-y} = c$

(viii) $y = \dfrac{A(x-1)}{x}$

(ix) not possible

(x) $y^3 = K - 3\cos x$

(xi) $y = A(x-2) - 2$

(xii) $\ln\left|\dfrac{x-8}{x}\right| = 8t + c$ or $x = \dfrac{8}{1 - Ae^{8t}}$

2 (i) $y = \dfrac{10}{1 - 10\ln x}$

(ii) $y = \dfrac{2}{1 - 2\ln x}$

(iii) $y^2 = \dfrac{2x^3 + 298}{3}$

(iv) $y = \ln\left(\dfrac{3 - \cos 2x}{2}\right)$

(v) $y = \ln\left(e^{10} + \dfrac{x^3}{3}\right)$

(vi) $e^{-y}(1 + y) = 3e^{-2} - x$

3 (i) $m = Ae^{-5t}$

(ii) $m = 10e^{-5t}$

4 (i) $P = Ae^{0.7t}$

(ii) $P = 100e^{0.7t}$

(iii) 0.99 minutes

5 (i) $v = \dfrac{20}{1 + 2t}$

(ii) 4.5 seconds

6 (i) $h = \dfrac{1}{\frac{\pi t}{4} + c}$ or $h = \dfrac{4}{\pi t + k}$

(ii) $t = \dfrac{4}{9\pi H}$

7 (i) $h = \left(2 - \dfrac{\sqrt{5}}{4}t\right)^2$

(ii) $t = \dfrac{8}{\sqrt{5}}$ (≈ 3.58) minutes to empty.

8 (i) $|10 - 0.2v| = Ae^{-0.2t}$

(ii) (a) $v = 50(1 - e^{-0.2t})$, 50

(b) $v = 50 + 30e^{-0.2t}$, 50

9 (i) $T = 20 + 80e^{-0.5t}$

(ii) $t = 1.96$ minutes

10 $v = \dfrac{40e^{-0.2t}}{41 - 40e^{-0.2t}}$

11 (i) $i = 0.2 - Ae^{-2500t}$

(ii) $i = 0.2(1 - e^{-2500t})$

(iii) $i = \dfrac{V}{R} - Ae^{-Rt/L}$

12 (ii) $t = 62.5\ln\left(\dfrac{2.5}{2.5 - h}\right)$

(iii) It takes an infinite time to fill the lock.

(iv) 446 seconds (to the nearest second).

13 (i) $v(0) = 0$

(iii)

(iv) $t = 11.09$ seconds

14 6 minutes before midnight.

15 (i) In running out at 8 litres per minute, salt is removed at a rate of $8C$ kg per minute and as the salt inflow is zero $\Rightarrow \dfrac{dM}{dt} = -8C$.

C kg of salt per litre $\Rightarrow 2000C$ kg of salt in the tank $\Rightarrow M = 2000C$.

(ii) $\dfrac{dC}{dt} = -0.004C$ **(iii)** 101 minutes

16 (i) $\dfrac{mg}{V}$

(iv) Air resistance reduces the maximum height by approximately $\dfrac{U^3}{3gV}$

17 (i) Initial conditions: $t = 0$, $v = 10$

(ii) $v = \sqrt{2500 - 2400e^{-t/25}}$

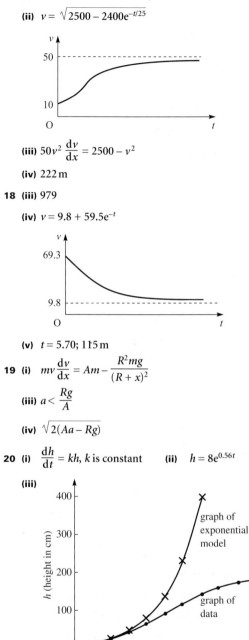

(iii) $50v^2 \dfrac{dv}{dx} = 2500 - v^2$

(iv) $222\,\text{m}$

18 (iii) 979

(iv) $v = 9.8 + 59.5e^{-t}$

(v) $t = 5.70$; $115\,\text{m}$

19 (i) $mv\dfrac{dv}{dx} = Am - \dfrac{R^2 mg}{(R+x)^2}$

(iii) $a < \dfrac{Rg}{A}$

(iv) $\sqrt{2(Aa - Rg)}$

20 (i) $\dfrac{dh}{dt} = kh$, k is constant   **(ii)** $h = 8e^{0.56t}$

(iii)

The exponential model suggests that sweet peas grow forever. The data show a limiting height.

(iv) When $h = H$, $\dfrac{dh}{dt} = 0$, i.e. an equilibrium height.

(v) $\dfrac{h}{H-h} = Ae^{at}$; $H = 190.8$, $A = 0.0438$;

$a = 0.616$, $h = \dfrac{190.8}{1 + 22.83e^{-0.616t}}$

(vi)

t	h
0	8.0
1	14.3
2	24.9
3	41.5
4	64.8
5	93.1
6	121.8
7	146.1
8	163.7
9	175.2
10	182.0

The logistic equation models the plant growth extremely well.

21 (i) $\dfrac{dS}{dt} = -kS(10^5 - S)$

(iii) $I = \dfrac{10^5}{1 + 99e^{-0.321t}}$

$S = \dfrac{9.9 \times 10^6 e^{-0.321t}}{1 + 99e^{-0.321t}}$

(v) 14.3 weeks

22 (iii) $P = R\rho T \Rightarrow P_0 = R\rho_0 T_0$

Second result follows from

$\dfrac{dP}{dz} = -\rho g$ and $\dfrac{\rho}{\rho_0} = \left(\dfrac{P}{P_0}\right)^m$

(iv) Yes. With $m = \frac{179}{180}$ then

$\dfrac{RT_0}{g(1-m)} = 45735 \approx 46000$

23 (i) The rate of increase of the volume of water in the cylinder $= A\dfrac{dx}{dt}\,\text{cm}^3\text{s}^{-1}$

The rate of decrease $= Bv\,\text{cm}^3\text{s}^{-1} \Rightarrow A\dfrac{dx}{dt} = -Bv$.

(ii) $x = \left(5 - \dfrac{\sqrt{1960}}{400}t\right)^2$

(iii) $(10 + x)\dfrac{dx}{dt} = -\dfrac{2\sqrt{1960}}{400}\sqrt{x}$

$t = \dfrac{550}{3} \times \dfrac{30}{2\sqrt{1960}} = 62.1\,\text{s}$

(iv) $A = 200\sqrt{x}$

24 (i) $x = 0$, $v = 0$

(ii) $v = 40(1 - e^{-0.25t})$

(iii) 25 s

(iv) 840 m

(v) 24 s, yes

Chapter 3

25 **(i)** $q = Q(1 - (1 - \lambda)e^{-kt})$

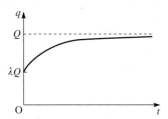

(iv) 40 minutes

The charge rate is proportional to the uncharged

part $\Rightarrow$ the uncharged part is halved as the charge

rate halves, i.e. 40 minutes

($\lambda = 0.4 \Rightarrow 0.6$ uncharged

$\lambda = 0.7 \Rightarrow 0.3$ uncharged $= \frac{1}{2} \times 0.6$)

26 **(i)** $v = 49(2e^{-0.2t} - 1)$

(ii) $T_1 = 5 \ln 2$

(iii) Down $\Rightarrow v < 0 \Rightarrow -0.02v > 0$ i.e. opposing

motion. The solution applies as it is the same

differential equation and has the same initial

conditions.

Chapter 4

? (Page 42)

Only **(i)**

? (Page 43)

(i) linear $P = -x^2, Q = x^2$

(ii) linear $P = x, Q = x^2$

(iii) linear $P = -(x + 1), Q = x^2 + x$

(iv) non-linear

? Activity (page 45)

(i) $\frac{d}{dx}(x^3 y) = 2e^x \Rightarrow x^3 y = 2e^x + c$

(ii) $\frac{d}{dx}(e^{3x} y) = x \Rightarrow e^{3x} y = \frac{1}{2}x^2 + c$

(iii) $\frac{d}{dx}\left(\frac{y}{x}\right) = x \Rightarrow \frac{y}{x} = \frac{1}{2}x^2 + c$

Exercise 4A (Page 49)

1 **(i)** $e^{\frac{1}{3}x^3}$

(ii) $e^{-\cos x}$

(iii) $x^{-\frac{1}{4}}$

(iv) x

(v) e^{7x}

(vi) $\sec x$

2 **(i)** $y = \frac{x^2}{4} - \frac{1}{4x^2}$

(ii) $y = 4 - 2e^{-\frac{1}{2}x^2}$

(iii) $y = 3e^{-3(x^2 - 1)}$

(iv) $y = \frac{1}{2}(3e^{x^2} - 1)$

(v) $y = x^3 - x^2$

(vi) $y = \frac{1}{3}(1 - 4e^{-x^3})$

3 **(i)** $v = 25 + Ae^{-0.4t}$

(ii) $v = 25(1 - e^{-0.4t})$

(v) The method of separation of variables is usually

preferred as it involves less work.

4 **(i)** $k = \frac{1}{3}$

(ii) $\frac{dv}{dt} = 10 - \frac{1}{3}v$

(iii) $v = 30 + Ae^{-\frac{1}{3}t}$

(iv) $v = 30(1 + e^{-\frac{1}{3}t})$

5 **(i)** $y = Ae^{-k_2 t} + \frac{k_1 a}{(k_2 - k_1)}e^{-k_1 t}$

(ii) $y = \frac{k_1 a}{(k_2 - k_1)}(e^{-k_1 t} - e^{-k_2 t})$

(iii) $\frac{dx}{dt} = -k_1 x, \frac{dz}{dt} = k_2 y$

(iv) $y = kat\,e^{-kt}$ where $k_1 = k_2 = k$.

6 **(i)** $\ln(\ln x) + c$

(ii) $\ln x$

(iii) $y = \frac{1}{2}\left(\ln x + \frac{1}{\ln x}\right)$

(iv)

7 **(i)** $I = I_0 e^{-t/RC}$

(ii) $I = \frac{\omega C E_0}{1 + (\omega RC)^2}(\cos \omega t + \omega RC \sin \omega t - e^{-t/RC})$

8 **(iii)** **(a)** $y = -\frac{1}{k}e^{-kx}\sin x + \frac{2}{k}\sin x$

For large x, $y \approx \frac{2}{k}\sin x$, oscillatory

(b) $y = -\frac{1}{k}e^{-kx}\sin x$

For large x, $y \approx 0$, oscillations decay

(iv) $y = (x + A)\sin x$

For large x, oscillations unbounded

9 (i) $x^2 y = A + \frac{1}{3}(1 + x^2)^{\frac{3}{2}}$

(ii) $x^2 y = \left(1 - \frac{2\sqrt{2}}{3}\right) + \frac{1}{3}(1 + x^2)^{\frac{3}{2}}$

$y \to \infty$ as $x \to 0$

(iii) $1 + \frac{3x^2}{2} + \frac{3x^4}{8}$

(iv) $y \approx \frac{A}{x^2} + \frac{1}{3x^2}\left(1 + \frac{3x^2}{2} + \frac{3x^4}{8} + ...\right)$

Take $A = -\frac{1}{3} \Rightarrow y = -\frac{1}{3x^2} + \frac{1}{3x^2}(1 + x^2)^{\frac{3}{2}}$

RHS of general solution is an even function of $x \Rightarrow$ solutions for $x > 0$ are symmetrical in the y axis $\Rightarrow$ many solutions for $x < 0$

10 (i) $y = \frac{1 - x}{1 + x}\left(A + x + \frac{x^2}{2}\right)$

(ii) (a) $y = \frac{1 - x}{1 + x}\left(x + \frac{x^2}{2}\right),\ y \to -\infty$

(b) $y = \frac{1 - x}{1 + x}\left(1 + x + \frac{x^2}{2}\right),\ y \to \infty$

(iii) $y = \frac{1}{2}(1 - x^2)$

11 (i) $t = 0,\ v = 0$

(ii) $v = \frac{49}{4}(1 - e^{-4t/5})$

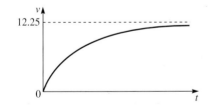

(iii) $v = \frac{9.8}{6}(t + 5) - 25\,520\frac{5}{6}(t + 5)^{-5}$

(iv)

12 (i) $y = -\cos x + \frac{\sin x}{x} + \frac{A}{x}$

(ii) $y = 1 + \frac{\pi - 2}{2\sqrt{2\pi}} \approx 1.128$

13 (ii) (a) $y = \frac{3 + 3x - x^3}{3(1 - x^4)}$

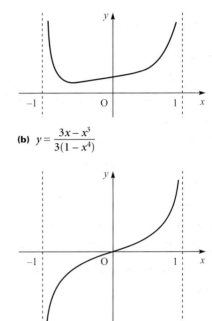

(b) $y = \frac{3x - x^3}{3(1 - x^4)}$

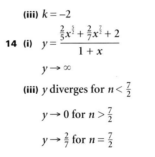

(iii) $k = -2$

14 (i) $y = \frac{\frac{2}{5}x^{\frac{5}{2}} + \frac{2}{7}x^{\frac{7}{2}} + 2}{1 + x}$

$y \to \infty$

(iii) y diverges for $n < \frac{7}{2}$

$y \to 0$ for $n > \frac{7}{2}$

$y \to \frac{2}{7}$ for $n = \frac{7}{2}$

Chapter 5

❓ (Page 53)

(i) $x^2 + y^2 = 4$; a circle centre O and radius 2

(ii) It should be a circle. Inaccuracies in using Euler's method have built up.

❓ Activity (Page 58)

See table 5.4 on page 59.

Exercise 5A (Page 58)

1 1.6319 with $h = 0.2$

1.6252 with $h = 0.1$

2 2.7387 with $h = 0.1$

2.7466 with $h = 0.05$

3 2.2666 with $h = 0.2$

2.2745 with $h = 0.1$

4 1.7680 with $h = 0.1$

1.8871 with $h = 0.05$

❓ (Page 60)

The straight line join of the plotted points for the two smallest values of h gives the best linear approximation to the curve as $h \to 0$.

Exercise 5B (Page 63)

1 (i)

h	$y(6)$
1.0	96
0.5	96.8
0.2	97.2672
0.1	97.4209

(ii) 97.5829

(iii) $y = 1280e^{-0.05(x-5)} + 80x - 1600$

$y(6) = 97.5737$ (to 4 d.p.)

(iv) $h \le 0.000\,32$

3125 steps

2 (i)

h	$y(2)$
0.2	1.1952
0.1	1.4205
0.05	1.8131
0.01	1.8982

(ii) 1.9324

(iii) $y(2) = 2$

(iv) $h \le 4.9 \times 10^{-6}$

200 000 steps

3 3.098

4 2.843

5 (i) 0.22

(ii)

The approximation improves as h gets smaller. From the graph, $y(1.2) \approx 0.239\,15$ but only $y(1.2) = 0.239$ can be justified (i.e. 3 d.p.).

6 (i) θ

(v)

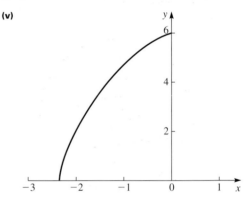

(vi) parabolic

7 (i) 0.1

(ii)

x_n	y_n	y'_n	y_{n+1}
0.5			0.4926
0.6	0.4926	0.6427	0.5569
0.7	0.5569	0.6101	0.6179
0.8	0.6179		

(iii)

(iv) The gradient is decreasing. For $x > 1$ the curve either turns upwards in which case $y'' > 0$ or the curve intersects $y^2 = x - 1$ in which case $y' = 0$ (a maximum) with y'' continuing to be negative.

(v) Less accurate as the error increases as h increases.

(vi) Less, because $y'' < 0$, for all h by this method.

8 (i) $\dfrac{p}{m - p} = Ae^{kt}$

(ii) 53 810

(iv)

t	p	p'
4.6		11 631.48
4.8	73 666.8	11 536.96
5.0	75 974	

9 (i) Circle, centre O, radius $\dfrac{1}{m}$

(ii), (iii)

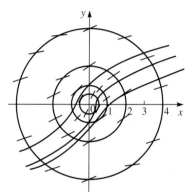

(iv)

x_n	y_n	y'_n
0	1	1
0.25	1.25	0.7845
0.5	1.4461	0.6535
0.75	1.6095	0.5632
1	1.7503	

(v) 1.6966

10 (i) $\dfrac{dy}{dx} = m \Rightarrow y = (m^2 + 1)x$

(ii) $y = x, \dfrac{dy}{dx} = 0$

$y = 1.5x, \dfrac{dy}{dx} = 0.7$

$y = 2x, \dfrac{dy}{dx} = 1$

$y = 3x, \dfrac{dy}{dx} = 1.4$

(i), (ii), (iii)

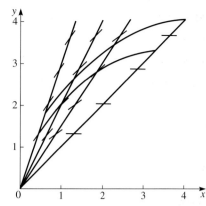

(iv)

x	y	y'
3.3	3.4202	0.1909
3.4	3.4393	0.1075
3.5	3.4501	

$y < x \Rightarrow y'$ not real, so no further

(v) Use negative h so x decreases.

x	y	y'
4.0	4	0
3.9	4	0.1601
3.8	3.9840	

11 (i) $k = 0.002; x = 0, v = 0$

(ii) $v^2 = 4900(1 - e^{-x/250})$

(iii)

depth $\approx 43\,\text{m}$

(iv)

x	v	$\dfrac{dv}{dx}$
42.5	5.74	−4.38
43.0	3.55	−7.29
43.5	−0.09	

$v = 0$ in $43 < x < 43.5$ so depth $= 43\,\text{m}$ (to the nearest metre). No, as the algorithm keeps increasing x, i.e. below greatest depth.

12 (ii)

θ	0	$\pm\dfrac{\pi}{12}$	$\pm\dfrac{\pi}{6}$	$\pm\dfrac{\pi}{4}$	$\pm\dfrac{\pi}{3}$
$\dfrac{d\theta}{dt}$	3.13	3.02	2.68	2.01	0

(ii), (iii)

(iv)

t	θ	$\dfrac{d\theta}{dt}$
0.40	0.997 28	0.913 64
0.45	1.042 96	0.267 96
0.50	1.056 36	

$1.056\,36 > \frac{\pi}{3}$ and so the final iteration has crossed the line $\theta = \frac{\pi}{3}$.

(v) When $\theta = -\frac{\pi}{3} \Rightarrow \frac{d\theta}{dt} = 0$ and so the algorithm will give constant $\theta (= -\frac{\pi}{3})$.

13 (i)

x_r	y_r	y_r'	y_{r+1}
1.4			4.3424
1.5	4.3424	5.6480	4.9072
1.6	4.9072	5.9424	5.5014
1.7	5.5014		

(ii)

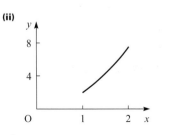

(iii) The gradient is increasing.

Each step underestimates the increase in y as it is based on the minimum gradient for the interval.

(iv) The argument of square root is negative.

14 (ii)

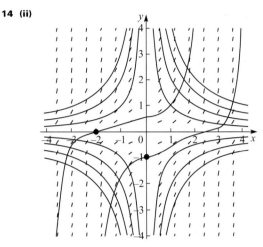

(iii) 0.080032; greater

Chapter 6

❓ (Page 70)

See text that follows.

❓ Activity (Page 73)

(i) $y = Ae^{-2x}$

(ii) $y = Ae^{2.5x}$

(iii) $x = Ae^{-\frac{1}{3}t}$

❓ (Page 73)

The general solution to a first order differential equation must contain one arbitrary constant and so $y = Ae^{-\frac{1}{3}x}$ is the general solution.

Exercise 6A (Page 74)

1 (i) $y = Ae^{3x}$

(ii) $y = Ae^{-7x}$

(iii) $x = Ae^{-t}$

(iv) $p = Ae^{0.02t}$

(v) $z = Ae^{0.2t}$

2 (i) $y = 3e^{-2x}$

(ii) $y = e^{\frac{3}{2}x}$

(iii) $x = 2e^{\frac{1}{3}(1-t)}$

(iv) $P = P_0 e^{kt}$

(v) $m = m_0 e^{-kt}$

3 $y = Ae^{-5x}$

4 (i) all three, $y = Ae^{17x}$

(ii) separation of variables only, $y = -\dfrac{1}{x+c}$

(iii) separation of variables or integrating factor,

$y = Ae^{-\frac{x^2}{2}}$

(iv) all three, $y = Ae^{3x}$

(v) all three (after division by y),

$y = Ae^x$ (which includes $y = 0$)

5 (i) $h(x, y)$ is a product (or quotient) of a function of

x alone and a function of y alone

(ii) $h(x, y)$ is linear in y

(iii) $h(x, y) = cy$ for some constant c

Exercise 6B (Page 77)

1 $y = Ae^{2x} + Be^x$

2 $y = Ae^{-x/3} + Be^{-x/2}$

3 $y = Ae^{x/2} + Be^{-x}$

4 $y = Ae^{-5x} + Be^x$

5 $y = Ae^{2x} + Be^{-2x}$

6 $y = Ae^x + Be^{2x} + Ce^{3x}$

7 $x = Ae^{-3t} + Be^{2t}$

8 $x = Ae^{3t} + Be^{-3t}$

9 $u = A + Be^{3t}$

10 $x = Ae^{\omega t} + Be^{-\omega t}$ where $\omega = \sqrt{\dfrac{k}{m}}$

Exercise 6C (Page 79)

1 $y = -2e^{3x} + 3e^{2x}$

$y \to -\infty$ as $x \to \infty$

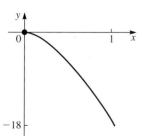

2 $y = \frac{1}{6}(e^{3x} - e^{-3x})$

$y \to \infty$ as $x \to \infty$

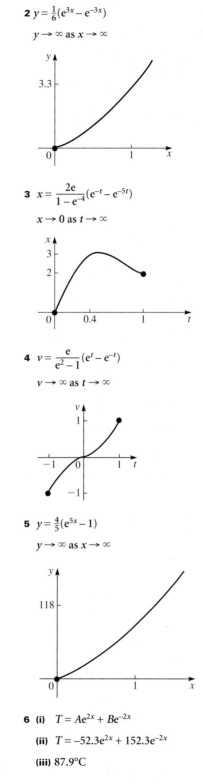

3 $x = \dfrac{2e}{1 - e^{-4}}(e^{-t} - e^{-5t})$

$x \to 0$ as $t \to \infty$

4 $v = \dfrac{e}{e^2 - 1}(e^t - e^{-t})$

$v \to \infty$ as $t \to \infty$

5 $y = \frac{4}{5}(e^{5x} - 1)$

$y \to \infty$ as $x \to \infty$

6 (i) $T = Ae^{2x} + Be^{-2x}$

(ii) $T = -52.3e^{2x} + 152.3e^{-2x}$

(iii) 87.9°C

? (Page 84)

(i) By first sketching the curves $y = e^{2x}$ and $y = -e^{2x}$ and fitting a curve between which touches the outer curves when $x = \dfrac{n\pi}{3}$ with ever increasing oscillations.

(ii) $\lambda^2 - 4\lambda + 13 = 0$

Exercise 6D (Page 85)

1 $x = \frac{1}{3}\sin 3t$

oscillating system, amplitude $\frac{1}{3}$, period $\dfrac{2\pi}{3}$

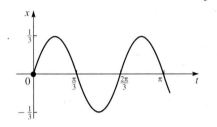

2 $x = 4\cos 0.5t$

oscillating system, amplitude 4, period 4π

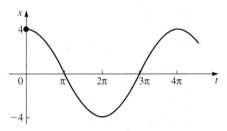

3 $x = \sin 2t$

oscillating system, amplitude 1, period π

4 $x = -9.47\sin 2\sqrt{3}t$

oscillating system, amplitude 9.47, period $\dfrac{\pi}{\sqrt{3}}$

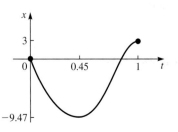

5 $x = \sqrt{\dfrac{m}{k}}\sin\sqrt{\dfrac{k}{m}}\,t$

oscillating system, amplitude $\sqrt{\dfrac{m}{k}}$, period $2\pi\sqrt{\dfrac{m}{k}}$

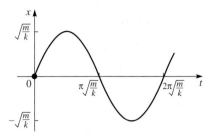

6 (i) $y = e^{2x}(A\sin x + B\cos x)$

(ii) $y = e^{x}(A\sin 2x + B\cos 2x)$

(iii) $x = e^{-t}(A\sin\sqrt{3}t + B\cos\sqrt{3}t)$

(iv) $x = e^{-0.5t}(A\sin t + B\cos t)$

7 (i) $y = 2e^{-x}\sin x$

decaying oscillations

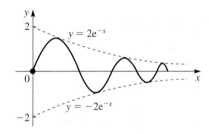

(ii) $y = e^{x}(2\cos\frac{1}{2}x - 4\sin\frac{1}{2}x)$

$\qquad = \sqrt{20}e^{x}\cos(\frac{x}{2} + 1.11)$

increasing oscillations

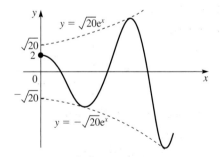

(iii) $y = 3e^{-x+\frac{\pi}{4}}\sin 2x = 6.58e^{-x}\sin 2x$ decaying oscillations

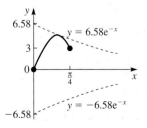

Answers (side margin)

(iv) $x = e^{1.5t}\left(\cos\dfrac{\sqrt{7}t}{2} - \dfrac{3}{\sqrt{7}}\sin\dfrac{\sqrt{7}t}{2}\right)$

$= 1.51e^{1.5t}\cos\left(\dfrac{\sqrt{7}}{2}t + 0.85\right)$

increasing oscillations

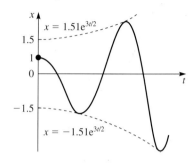

❓ Activity (Page 87)

$y = (A + Bx + Cx^2)e^{ax}$

Exercise 6E (Page 87)

1 (i) $y = Ae^{4x} + Be^{-4x}$

(ii) $x = A\sin\omega t + B\cos\omega t$

(iii) $y = Ae^{1.79x} + Be^{-2.79x}$

(iv) $x = e^{-\frac{t}{6}}\left(A\sin\dfrac{\sqrt{23}}{6}t + B\cos\dfrac{\sqrt{23}}{6}t\right)$

(v) $y = e^{4x}(Ax + B)$

(vi) $x = Ae^{-1.71t} + Be^{-0.29t}$

(vii) $y = A + Be^{-\frac{2}{7}x}$

(viii) $y = e^{\frac{2}{3}x}(Ax + B)$

(ix) $r^2 > 4km$

$x = Ae^{(\alpha + \beta)t} + Be^{(\alpha - \beta)t}\begin{cases}\alpha = -\dfrac{r}{2m}\\[2mm]\beta = \dfrac{\sqrt{r^2 - 4km}}{2m}\end{cases}$

$r^2 = 4km \quad x = e^{-rt/(2m)}(At + B)$

$r^2 < 4km$

$x = e^{-rt/(2m)}\left(A\sin\dfrac{\sqrt{4km - r^2}}{2m}t\right.$

$\left. + B\cos\dfrac{\sqrt{4km - r^2}}{2m}t\right)$

(x) $x = Ae^{2t} + Be^{-2t} + C\sin2t + D\cos2t$

3 (i) $x = \dfrac{\sqrt{2}}{4}\sin2\sqrt{2}t + \cos2\sqrt{2}t$

$= \dfrac{3\sqrt{2}}{4}\sin(2\sqrt{2}t + 1.23)$

oscillations with constant amplitude

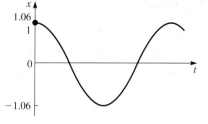

(ii) $x = \frac{4}{5}(1 - e^{-5t})$

initially moves quickly towards its limiting position

position $x = 0.8$

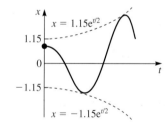

(iii) $x = e^{t/2}\left(\cos\dfrac{\sqrt{3}}{2}t - \dfrac{1}{\sqrt{3}}\sin\dfrac{\sqrt{3}}{2}t\right)$

$= \dfrac{2}{\sqrt{3}}e^{t/2}\cos\left(\dfrac{\sqrt{3}}{2}t + 0.52\right)$

exponentially increasing oscillations

4 (i) $y = 2xe^{1-x}$

(ii) $x = (1 - 3t)e^{3t}$

(iii) $x = 2(2 - t)e^{-0.5t}$

(iv) $y = 2xe^{-kx}$

❓ (Page 91)

(i) $y = ax^2 + bx + c$

(ii) $y = l\sin4x + m\cos4x$

(iii) $y = ce^{-0.5x}$

❓ Activity (Page 95)

$c = \frac{1}{2}, d = 0$

Exercise 6F (Page 95)

1 $y = -2x - 5$

2 $x = \frac{1}{4}t + \frac{1}{2}$

3 $y = \frac{5}{3}x + \frac{2}{9}$

4 $x = \dfrac{l}{\omega^2}$

5 $v = -\frac{1}{2}t - \frac{3}{2}$

6 $y = \frac{1}{2}x^2 - 7x$

7 $y = -0.08\cos3x + 0.06\sin3x$

8 $y = -\frac{1}{289}(8\cos4x + 15\sin4x)$

9 $v = -0.2\cos t - 0.6\sin t$

10 $x = 0.6\cos2t$

11 $x = -\dfrac{1}{4 + \omega^2}\sin\omega t$

12 $x = \frac{1}{2}\cos t + \frac{1}{4}\sin t$

13 $y = \frac{1}{5}e^{-x}$

14 $x = \frac{3}{4}e^{-2t}$

15 $y = -5e^{2x}$

16 $x = \frac{1}{12}e^{-3t}$

Exercise 6G (Page 97)

1 (i) $y = A\cos2x + B\sin2x + \frac{1}{5}e^x + \frac{1}{8}e^{2x}$

(ii) $x = Ae^{3t} + Be^{-t} + e^{-2t} + 2e^{4t}$

(iii) $y = A\cos\sqrt{2}x + B\sin\sqrt{2}x + e^x + \sin x$

(iv) $y = e^{-0.5x}\left(A\cos\dfrac{\sqrt{3}}{2}x + B\sin\dfrac{\sqrt{3}}{2}x\right) + 4 + \sin x$

(v) $y = e^{-0.5x}\left(A\cos\dfrac{\sqrt{3}}{2}x + B\sin\dfrac{\sqrt{3}}{2}x\right)$
$\qquad + 3x - 1 + \frac{1}{3}e^x$

(vi) $y = A\cos x + B\sin x - \frac{1}{2}x\cos x$

(vii) $y = Ae^{-4x} + Be^x + \frac{1}{5}xe^x$

(viii) $y = Ae^x + Be^{3x} - xe^x + \frac{1}{2}xe^{3x}$

(ix) $y = (Ax + B)e^{3x} + 2x^2e^{3x}$

(x) $y = A + Be^{2x} - \frac{1}{4}x^2 - \frac{1}{4}x$

2 (i) $y = -6e^{3x} + e^{2x} + 6x + 5$

(ii) $x = -2\cos3t + \sin3t + 2e^{-t}$

(iii) $y = e^{-x}(-\cos2x + 1)$

(iv) $x = -e^{-2t} + 4e^t - \cos2t - 3\sin2t$

(v) $y = 2 - e^{-x} + \frac{1}{2}x^2 - x$

(vi) $x = \frac{1}{2}e^{2t} - e^t + \frac{1}{2} + te^t$

(vii) $y = 2\sin2x - 3x\cos2x$

(viii) $y = e^{-2x}(2\cos x + 3\sin x) - \cos x + \sin x$

(ix) $y = \frac{1}{2}e^{-2x} + \frac{1}{2}e^{2x} + x - 1$

(x) $\frac{1}{2}(x + 1)^2e^{-2x}$

3 (i) $p = Ae^{-t}$

(ii) $p = 100 - 25(\cos t - \sin t)$

(iii) $p = 100 - 25(\cos t - \sin t) - 55e^{-t}$

(iv) 100

(v) $25\sqrt{2}$

4 (i) $\dfrac{dv}{dx} + v\tan x = e^{-x}\cos x$

(ii) $v = -e^{-x}\cos x + \frac{3}{2}\cos x$

(iii) $y = \frac{1}{2}e^{-x}(\cos x - \sin x) + \frac{3}{2}\sin x + \frac{1}{2}$

(iv) $\dfrac{3\sqrt{2}}{4} + \dfrac{1}{2}$

5 (i) $y = Ae^{-x} + Be^{-2x} + x - 1$

(ii) $y = e^{-2x} - e^{-x} + x - 1$

(iii) $y'' = 0 \Rightarrow x = \ln4 \approx 1.39$

(iv)

6 (i) **(a)** $y = e^{-x}(A\sin3x + B\cos3x + 2)$

(b) $y = e^{-x}(2 - 2\cos3x)$

(c) $x = \dfrac{2\pi}{3}, \dfrac{4\pi}{3}$

(ii) $y = e^{-x}(A\sin3x + B\cos3x) + C$

7 (ii) **(a)** $V = e^{-t}(A\sin2t + B\cos2t)$

(b) $V = -\frac{2}{25} + \frac{1}{5}t + \frac{1}{4}e^{-t}$

(c) $V = e^{-t}\left(A\sin2t + B\cos2t + \frac{1}{4}\right) - \frac{2}{25} + \frac{1}{5}t$

8 (i) $y = (A + Bt)e^{-2t}$

(ii) They satisfy the homogeneous equation.

$y = at^2e^{-2t}$

(iii) $A = 3, B = -4$

$y = (t-1)(t-3)e^{-2t}$

(iv) (a) $y = (t-2)(t-7)e^{-2t}$

(b) $y = (t-1)^2e^{-2t}$

e.g. $y = (t^2+1)e^{-2t}$; $t^2+1 > 0$, $e^{-2t} > 0$

9 (i) $y = Ae^{-t} + Be^{-2t} + \frac{1}{10}\sin t - \frac{3}{10}\cos t$

$y = \frac{1}{2}e^{-t} - \frac{1}{5}e^{-2t} + \frac{1}{10}\sin t - \frac{3}{10}\cos t$

(ii) $y = Ae^{-t} + Be^{-2t} + \frac{1}{10}e^t(\sin t - \cos t)$

(iii) Both oscillate; bounded for $k = 0$, unbounded

for $k = 1$.

When $k = -1$ the solution tends to zero.

10 (i) $I = -\frac{3}{5}\sin t + \frac{4}{5}\cos t + (A + Bt)e^{-2t}$

(iii) Amplitude $= 1$

$R = 1, a = 0.6435$

(iv) $0.493, 0.719$

11 (i) $I = e^{-\frac{1}{10}t}\left(20 + A\cos\frac{3}{10}t + B\sin\frac{3}{10}t\right)$

(ii) $I = 20e^{-\frac{1}{10}t}\left(1 - \cos\frac{3}{10}t\right)$

(iv) $I' = De^{-\frac{1}{\sqrt{10}}t} + (C + Dt)\left(-\frac{1}{\sqrt{10}}\right)e^{-\frac{1}{\sqrt{10}}t}$

$a > -\frac{4}{\sqrt{10}}$

12 (i) $y = Ae^{-2t}$

(ii) It satisfies the homogeneous equation.

$y = te^{-2t}$

(iii) $y = te^{-2t} + Ae^{-2t}$

(iv) $y_0 < \frac{1}{2}$

13 (i) $y = \dfrac{xe^x - e^x + c}{x}$

(ii) $y \to 0$

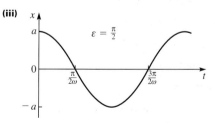

(iii) $y = Ae^{-x} + \frac{1}{2}e^x$

(iv) $y = 1 - Ae^{-e^x}$

14 (i) $y = Ae^x + Be^{-2x} - 6e^{-x}$

(ii) $y = 2e^{-2x} - 6e^{-x}$

(iii) $x = -\ln 3$

Chapter 7

❓ (Page 103)

See text that follows.

❓ Activity (Page 108)

$x = a\sin\omega t$

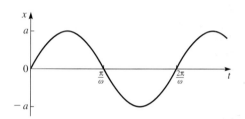

❓ Activity (Page 109)

(i)

(ii)

(iii)

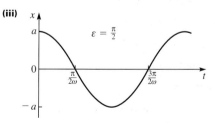

In each case the frequency is $\dfrac{\omega}{2\pi}$ and is unaffected by

ε, which shifts the sine curve to the left by $\dfrac{\varepsilon}{\omega}$.

❓ Activity (Page 109)

$A\sin\omega t + B\cos\omega t \equiv a\cos(\omega t - \varepsilon_1)$

$\Rightarrow \tan\varepsilon_1 = \dfrac{A}{B}, a = \sqrt{A^2 + B^2}$

Exercise 7A (Page 112)

1 (i) $\dfrac{d^2x}{dt^2} + 64x = 0 \quad \dfrac{dx}{dt} = 0, x = 0.1$ when $t = 0$

(ii) $x = 0.1\cos 8t$

(iii) period $= \dfrac{\pi}{4}$ s, amplitude $= 0.1$ m

(iv)

2 (i) 0.357 m

(ii) $\dfrac{d^2x}{dt^2} + 62.5x = 0$

$\dfrac{dx}{dt} = 0, x = 0.1$ when $t = 0$

(iii) $x = 0.1\cos\sqrt{62.5}t$

(iv) period $= \dfrac{2\pi}{\sqrt{62.5}} = 0.79$ s,

amplitude $= 0.1$ m (10 cm)

3 (i) 0.039 m

(ii) $l = 0.439 + 0.03\cos\sqrt{250}t$

4 period $= \dfrac{2\pi}{\sqrt{250}} = 0.397$ s

5 (i) $\dfrac{5\pi}{180} = 0.0873$ radians

(ii) period $= 3.48$ s

(iii) $a = 0.087, \omega = 1.807, \varepsilon = 0$

(iv) maximum speed $= 0.473$ ms^{-1}

6 (i) length $= \dfrac{g}{\pi^2} = 0.993$ m.

(ii) (a) no change

(b) increases the period by a factor $\sqrt{2}$

(c) no change

(d) increases the period by a factor $\sqrt{6}$

7 (i) $\dfrac{d^2\theta}{dt^2} = -\dfrac{g}{4}\sin\theta$

neglect air resistance

inextensible string

no friction at support

small angle vibrations ($\sin\theta \approx \theta$)

bob is a particle

(ii) period $= 4.01$ s

8 (i) net force $= 0$ and only forces when in equilibrium are F and mg.

constant $= \dfrac{mg}{l}$

(ii) $F = \dfrac{mg}{l}(l + x), \dfrac{d^2x}{dt^2} + \dfrac{g}{l}x = 0$

(iii) $2\pi\sqrt{\dfrac{l}{g}}$

9 (i) $V = \dfrac{2\pi}{3} = 2.1$ ms^{-1}

(ii) 0.87 m

(iii) 0.022 N

❓ (Page 119)

(i) no damping

(ii) underdamping

(iii) any form of damping but close to critical damping for a quick reading, e.g. the scales at a supermarket check-out

(iv) overdamping but close to critical damping

Exercise 7B (Page 120)

1 (i) $\dfrac{d^2x}{dt^2} + 80x = 0, \dfrac{dx}{dt} = 0$ and $x = 0.1$ when $t = 0$

(ii) $x = 0.1\cos\sqrt{80}t.$

(iii)

(iv) For critical damping, damping

constant $= \sqrt{20}(\approx 4.47)$

(v) for $m = 0.3$, underdamped system for $m = 0.2$, overdamped system

2 (i) $x = e^{-1.5t}A\cos\left(\dfrac{\sqrt{31}}{2}t + \varepsilon\right) + 0.05$

(ii) $x = 0.057e^{-1.5t}\cos(2.78t - 0.49) + 0.05$

$x \to 0.05$ as $t \to \infty$

(iii) 1.16

3 (i) $q = (2 + 9t)e^{-2.5t}$

(ii)

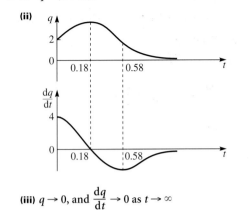

(iii) $q \to 0$, and $\dfrac{dq}{dt} \to 0$ as $t \to \infty$

4 (i) $T = 37.3 + 12.7e^{-0.5t}$

(ii) $T = 42.0°C$

(iii)

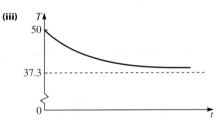

(iv) 37.3°C

5 (i) $\theta = e^{-2t}A\cos(t + \varepsilon)$

(ii) $\theta = 1.76e^{-2t}\cos(t - 1.11)$

(iii) The motion effectively ends at about $t = 2.5$.
Although θ subsequently does become negative.
The amplitude of the oscillation is very small and
decreases rapidly.

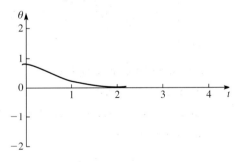

(iv) $\theta \to 0$ as $t \to \infty$

6 (i) $10^4 \dfrac{d^2x}{dt^2} + 2 \times 10^5 \dfrac{dx}{dt} + 10^6 x = 0$

where x is depression of spring from its natural
length; $\dfrac{dx}{dt} = 5$, $x = 0$ when $t = 0$, $x = 5te^{-10t}$

(ii)

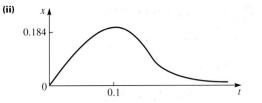

The buffer is compressed 18.4 cm after 0.1 s and is
then gradually released.

7 (i) (a) $x = 4 - \dfrac{20}{3}e^{-t} + \dfrac{8}{3}e^{-2.5t}$

(b) $x = 4.9 - (7.01t + 4.9)e^{-1.43t}$

(c) $x = 8 - e^{-0.875t}(10.0\sin0.70t + 8\cos0.70t)$

$= 8 - 12.8e^{-0.875t}\cos(0.70t - 0.90)$

(ii)

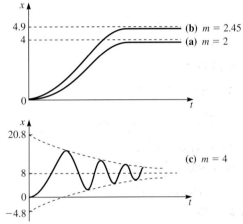

8 (i) $\rho = \dfrac{4m}{3\pi a^2 b}$

(ii) $m\dfrac{d^2x}{dt^2}$ = mass multiplied by downward
acceleration

$2mk\dfrac{dx}{dt}$ = resistance to motion

$\dfrac{4mg}{3b}x$ = extra upward thrust of $\pi a^2 x \rho g$ from
displaced water whose volume is $\pi a^2 x$.

(iv) $x = e^{-kt}\left(\dfrac{b}{4}\cos\omega t + \dfrac{kb}{4\omega}\sin\omega t\right)$

(v)

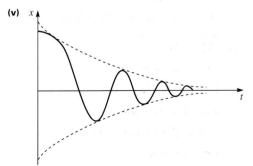

9 (ii) $x = A\sin\omega t + B\cos\omega t + \dfrac{c}{\omega^2}$.

$\dfrac{c}{\omega^2}$ is the value of x when the system is in equilibrium.

(iii) When $r > 2\omega$, $x = Ae^{\lambda_1 t} + Be^{\lambda_2 t} + \dfrac{c}{\omega^2}$

where λ_1, λ_2 are the real roots of $\lambda^2 + r\lambda + \omega^2 = 0$.

When $r = 2\omega$, $x = (At + B)e^{-rt/2} + \dfrac{c}{\omega^2}$

When $r < 2\omega$,

$x = e^{-rt/2}(A\sin\Omega t + B\cos\Omega t) + \dfrac{c}{\omega^2}$

where $\Omega = \dfrac{\sqrt{4\omega^2 - r^2}}{2}$.

10 (i) $10\dfrac{dv}{dt} = k(y - 0.5) - 4v$

(ii) $y = \dfrac{3}{2} + e^{-t/5}\left(A\sin\dfrac{7t}{5} + B\cos\dfrac{7t}{5}\right)$

(iii) $y = \dfrac{3}{2} + e^{-t/5}\left(\dfrac{24}{7}\sin\dfrac{7t}{5} - \cos\dfrac{7t}{5}\right)$

(iv) $y \to \dfrac{3}{2}$, $v \to 5$ v is unaffected, but y increases as the PI is now $0.5 + \dfrac{20}{k}$, since for large t, $y \to 0.5 + \dfrac{20}{k}$ which is $> \dfrac{3}{2}$ for $k < 20$.

11 (i) $y = e^{-2t}(A\sin5t + B\cos5t) + \dfrac{1}{4}\sin5t - \dfrac{5}{4}\cos5t$

(iii) $y = 0 \Rightarrow$ smallest $t = \dfrac{1}{5}\arctan5 = 0.275$

(iv) $\dfrac{\sqrt{26}}{4} = 1.27$

Chapter 8

❓ (Page 124)

(i) When she sings she produces a sound wave of just the same frequency as that for a natural vibration of the glass. As a result the glass vibrates so strongly that it breaks.

(ii) In theory you can make this happen. However, you need a strong voice and to be able to hit just the right note for the glass.

Exercise 8A (Page 132)

1 (ii) $x = 0.5 + \dfrac{1}{50 - \Omega^2}(5\cos\Omega t - 0.1\Omega^2\cos\sqrt{50}t)$

(iii)

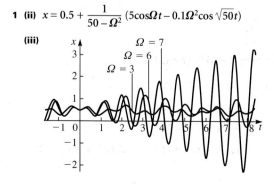

(iv) $\Omega = \sqrt{50}$ for resonance

$x = 0.5 + \dfrac{t}{2\sqrt{2}}\sin\sqrt{50}t + 0.1\cos\sqrt{50}t$

2 (i) $q = \dfrac{10(100\sin\Omega t - \Omega\sin100t)}{10\,000 - \Omega^2}$

(ii) $\Omega = 100$ for resonance

$q = 0.05\sin100t - 5t\cos100t$

$t = 2000\text{s }(636.63\pi)$

(iii)

3 (i) $y = A\sin\omega t + B\cos\omega t + \dfrac{F\omega^2}{\omega^2 - p^2}\sin pt \ (p \neq \omega)$

(ii) $y = \cos\omega t + \dfrac{\omega F}{(\omega^2 - p^2)}(\omega\sin pt - p\sin\omega t)$

(iii)

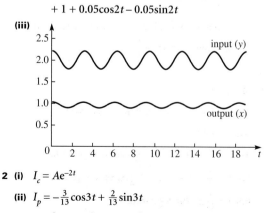

❓ Activity (Page 137)

See key points on page 141.

Exercise 8B (Page 138)

1 (ii) $x = e^{-1.5t}(-0.05\cos2.78t + 0.009\sin2.78t)$
$+ 1 + 0.05\cos2t - 0.05\sin2t$

(iii)

2 (i) $I_c = Ae^{-2t}$

(ii) $I_p = -\dfrac{3}{13}\cos3t + \dfrac{2}{13}\sin3t$

(iii) $I = \dfrac{3}{13}e^{-2t} - \dfrac{3}{13}\cos3t + \dfrac{2}{13}\sin3t$

(iv) $\dfrac{1}{\sqrt{13}} = 0.277$

3 (i) $e^{-t}(A\sin 3t + B\cos 3t)$

(ii) underdamped system

(iii) $\dfrac{(10 - \omega^2)\sin\omega t - 2\omega\cos\omega t}{(10 - \omega^2)^2 + 4\omega^2}$

4 (i) $e^{-50t}(A\sin 50\sqrt{3}t + B\cos 50\sqrt{3}t)$

(ii) underdamped

(iii) $-0.1\cos 100t$,

$q = e^{-50t}(A\sin 50\sqrt{3}t + B\cos 50\sqrt{3}t) - 0.1\cos 100t$

(iv) $A = \dfrac{1}{10\sqrt{3}}$, $B = \dfrac{1}{10}$

(v)

5 (i) $x = B\sin\omega t + C\cos\omega t$

(ii) damping term, forcing term

(iii) $x = B\sin\omega t + C\cos\omega t + \dfrac{A}{\omega^2 - a^2}\cos at$

(iv) The closer a gets to ω, the larger the amplitude of the vibrations.

6 (i) $x = \dfrac{m^2 g}{a^2 r^2}(e^{-rat/m} - 1) + \dfrac{mg}{ar}t$

$v = \dfrac{mg}{ar}(1 - e^{-rat/m})$

(ii)

Speed of sphere increases until it reaches its terminal velocity $\dfrac{mg}{ar}$.

7 (i) $k = 1$

(ii) $x = 1 - (t + 1)e^{-t}$

(iii) $x = 1 - e^{-0.6t}(0.75\sin 0.8t + \cos 0.8t)$

(iv) $1 + e^{-0.75\pi} = 1.095$.

8 (i) $I = Ae^{-5t} + Be^{-20t} + \frac{3}{20}\sin 20t + \frac{1}{4}\cos 20t$

(ii) $I = \frac{17}{60}e^{-20t} - \frac{8}{15}e^{-5t} + \frac{3}{20}\sin 20t + \frac{1}{4}\cos 20t$

(iii) $I = \frac{3}{20}\sin 20t + \frac{1}{4}\cos 20t$

The terms $Ae^{-5t} + Be^{-20t}$ decay whatever the values of A and B.

(iv) $R = \dfrac{\sqrt{34}}{20}$ $\quad a = 1.030$

9 (i) $x = A\sin 14t + B\cos 14t$

(ii) $\lambda = \dfrac{2}{196 - \omega^2}$, $\mu = 0$

$x = A\sin 14t + B\cos 14t + \dfrac{2}{196 - \omega^2}\sin\omega t$

(iii) (a) The form in part (ii) satisfies $\ddot{x} + 196x = 0$

$x = -\dfrac{t}{14}\cos 14t$

$x = -\dfrac{t}{14}\cos 14t + A\sin 14t + B\cos 14t$

(b) $x = -\dfrac{t}{14}\cos 14t + \dfrac{1}{196}\sin 14t$

oscillations unbounded (resonance)

10 (ii) $x = A\sin 5t + B\cos 5t$

$x = 0.2\cos 5t$

(iii) $x = 0.01\sin 5t - 0.05t\cos 5t$

The oscillations are unbounded

(iv) Resistance opposes motion.

$0 < k < 10$

Chapter 9

❓ Activity (page 150)

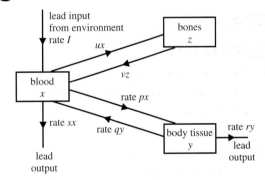

$\dfrac{dx}{dt} = I - (p + s + u)x + qy + vz$

$\dfrac{dy}{dt} = px - (q + r)y$

$\dfrac{dz}{dt} = ux - vz$

Exercise 9A (Page 158)

1 (i) (a) $x = Ae^{2t} + Be^{t}$

$y = Ae^{2t} + 2Be^{t}$

(b) $x = e^{t}$, $y = 2e^{t}$

(c) $(x, y) \to \infty$ as $t \to \infty$ along the line $y = 2x$

(ii) (a) $x = Ae^{\sqrt{2}t} + Be^{-\sqrt{2}t}$

$y = (\sqrt{2} - 1)Ae^{\sqrt{2}t} - (\sqrt{2} + 1)Be^{-\sqrt{2}t}$

(b) $x = 1.56e^{\sqrt{2}t} - 0.56^{-\sqrt{2}t}$

$y = 0.65e^{\sqrt{2}t} + 1.35e^{-\sqrt{2}t}$

(c) $(x, y) \to \infty$ as $t \to \infty$ along the line $y = 0.42x$

(iii) (a) $x = e^t(A\sin\sqrt{6}t + B\cos\sqrt{6}t) + 1$

$y = \dfrac{\sqrt{6}e^t}{2}(-B\sin\sqrt{6}t + A\cos\sqrt{6}t) + 1$

(b) $x = 1 + \dfrac{\sqrt{6}}{2}e^t\sin\sqrt{6}t$

$y = 1 + e^t\cos\sqrt{6}t$

(c)   Spirals away from $(1, 2)$ to ∞

(iv) (a) $x = Ae^{5t} + Be^{-t}$

$y = Ae^{5t} - Be^{-t}$

(b) $x = \frac{1}{2}(3e^{5t} - e^{-t})$

$y = \frac{1}{2}(3e^{5t} + e^{-t})$

(c) $(x, y) \to \infty$ as $t \to \infty$ along $y = x$

(v) (a) $x = e^{-t}(A\sin t + B\cos t)$

$y = \dfrac{e^{-t}}{5}[(A - 2B)\cos t - (2A + B)\sin t]$

(b) $x = e^{-t}(12\sin t + \cos t)$

$y = e^{-t}(2\cos t - 5\sin t)$

(c) $(x, y) \to (0, 0)$ as $t \to \infty$

(vi) (a) $x = e^{2t}(A + Bt) + 2$, $y = -Be^{2t} + 3$

(b) $x = 2 + (t - 1)e^{2t}$, $y = 3 - e^{2t}$

(c) $x \to \infty$, $y \to -\infty$ as $t \to \infty$

2 $a > b + c$, $\dfrac{T}{T + F} \to \dfrac{a - b - c}{a - c}$

3 (i) $x = 8e^{-4t}$

$y = 16e^{-2t} - 16e^{-4t}$

$z = 8e^{-4t} - 16e^{-2t} + 8$

(ii)   4

(iii) $z \to 8$ as $t \to \infty$

4 (i) $x = e^{-0.5t}$

(ii) $y = 2.5(e^{-0.3t} - e^{-0.5t})$

(iii) $z = 1.5e^{-0.5t} - 2.5e^{-0.3t} + 1$

5 (ii) $x = e^{0.01t}(49\,900t + 10\,000)$

(iii) $y = e^{0.01t}(49\,900t + 5\,000\,000)$

(iv) $x = 273\,000$

$y = 5.52$ million

6 (ii) $C_1 = 2.4 + 0.6e^{-0.05t}$

(iii) $C_2 = 2.4 - 2.4e^{-0.05t}$

(iv)   After 4 hours, $C_1 = 2.89$, $C_2 = 0.435$

As $t \to \infty$, $C_1 \to \frac{12}{5}$, $C_2 \to \frac{12}{5}$

7 (i) $-5, -13$

(iii) $x = 5.75e^{-t} + 0.25e^{3t} - 2$

(iv) $y = 11.5e^{-t} - 0.5e^{3t} - 5$

8 (ii) $x = Ae^{-0.054t} + Be^{-0.026t} + 536$

(iii) $y = -0.4Ae^{-0.054t} + 2.4Be^{-0.026t} + 179$

(iv) $x = -395.5e^{-0.054t} - 140.5e^{-0.026t} + 536$

$y = 158.2e^{-0.054t} - 337.2e^{-0.026t} + 179$

(v) $x = 536\ \mu g$, $y = 179\ \mu g$

9 (i) $0, -20$

(ii) $\dfrac{d^2x}{dt^2} - 3\dfrac{dx}{dt} - 4x = 0$

(iii) $x = 3e^{4t} + 12e^{-t}$

(iv) $y = 12e^{-t} - 2e^{4t}$

(v)   The second species becomes extinct after nearly 36 years

10 $q = 2e^{-t} - 2e^{-2t}$

11 $\dfrac{dp}{dt} = kp$, $\dfrac{dq}{dt} = 2kq$, $45\,g$

12 (i) k^2aP_0

(ii) $\ddot{V} - k^2a^2V = 0$

(iii) $V = Ae^{kat} + Be^{-kat}$

(iv) $P = \dfrac{1}{2k}\{(V_0 + kP_0)e^{kat} - (V_0 - kP_0)e^{-kat}\}$

(v) $t = 4\ln(3.5226) = 5.04$

13 (i) $p = \frac{28}{5}$, $q = 7$

(iii) $p = Ae^{-10t} + Be^{-3t} + \frac{28}{5}$

$p = \frac{28}{5} - \frac{3}{5}e^{-10t} - 5e^{-3t}$

$q = 7 + 3e^{-10t} - 10e^{-3t}$

(iv)

$$p \to \tfrac{28}{5} = 5.6, \quad q \to 7$$

14 (ii) $r = Ae^{0.2t} + Be^{0.8t}$

(iii) $A = \tfrac{40}{3}f_0 - 4000, \quad B = 16\,000 - \tfrac{40}{3}f_0$

$r = \left(\tfrac{40}{3}f_0 - 4000\right)e^{\frac{t}{5}} + \left(1600 - \tfrac{400}{3}f_0\right)e^{\frac{4t}{5}}$

$f = \left(\tfrac{4}{3}f_0 - 400\right)e^{\frac{t}{5}} + \left(40 - \tfrac{1}{3}f_0\right)e^{\frac{4t}{5}}$

(v) $\dfrac{df}{dt} = \dfrac{r}{50}$ so $r > 0 \Rightarrow \dfrac{df}{dt} > 0$ so the foxes cannot die out first.

15 (i) $x = Ae^{-2t}$

(iii) Maximum $y = 2.5$ when $e^t = 2$

(v) $y = -5e^{-2t} - 1.5t + 5.34$

Maximum $y = 3.16$ when $t = 0.9486$

16 (i) $x = 5e^{-2t}$

(ii) $y = 5e^{-2t} - 5e^{-4t}$

(iii) $y = \tfrac{5}{4}$ when $t = \tfrac{1}{2}\ln 2$

$y \to 0$ as $t \to \infty$

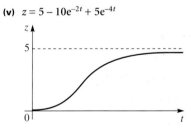

(iv) No loss of mass in total

(v) $z = 5 - 10e^{-2t} + 5e^{-4t}$

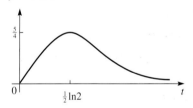

17 (ii) $x = 200 - 125e^{-0.01t} - 75e^{-0.05t}$

(iii) $x = Ae^{-0.01t} + Be^{-0.05t}$

$y = 3Ae^{-0.01t} - Be^{-0.05t}$

If $x = y = 0$ then on adding $4Ae^{-0.01t} = 0 \Rightarrow A = 0$ and hence $B = 0$ implying that both x and y are always zero. But at the start the fish is polluted

and so, at time $t = 0$, x and y are not both zero which means that at any finite time it is not possible for both x and y to be zero. So the fish is never clear of pollution.

18 (ii) $x = e^{-5t}(A\sin t + B\cos t)$

$y = \tfrac{1}{10}e^{-5t}((7A + B)\sin t + (7B - A)\cos t)$

19 (i) $x = 25e^{-0.1t}$

(ii) $y = 25(e^{-0.1t} - e^{-0.2t})$

(iii) $t < 10\ln 2 \approx 6.93$

(iv) $z = 25(1 - 2e^{-0.1t} + e^{-0.2t})$

20 (i) $w = 2000e^{2t}$

Population grows without limit.

Unlikely as growth will be limited by factors such as space or disease.

(ii) (a) $\dfrac{w}{x} > 40$

(b) $\dfrac{w}{x} > 100$

(c) $40 < \dfrac{w}{x} < 100$

(iii) $w = 2441, \quad x = 24.81$

(iv) The actual number of foxes must be integers but the values are not. Modelled as continuous change, whereas actual changes are discrete.

21 (ii) $x = 10 - \tfrac{8}{5}e^{-7t} - \tfrac{42}{5}e^{-2t}$

$y = 12 + \tfrac{24}{5}e^{-7t} - \tfrac{84}{5}e^{-2t}$

(iii)

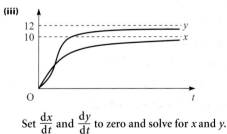

Set $\dfrac{dx}{dt}$ and $\dfrac{dy}{dt}$ to zero and solve for x and y.

22 (ii) $x = -21\sin t + 3\cos t + Ae^{3t} + Be^{-2t}$

(iii) $x = -21\sin t + 3\cos t - 3e^{-2t}$

$y = -31\sin t + 33\cos t - 18e^{-2t}$

23 (ii) $y = 12 - e^{-6t} - 7e^{-t}$

(iii) Increasing

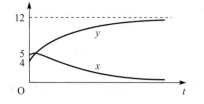

(iv) $-3.66 \, \text{km}^3$ per day

24 Equilibrium values for (P, Q) are $(25.8, 774.6)$ and $(-25.8, -774.6)$. Only $(25.8, 774.6)$ is possible.

25 Equilibrium values for (F, R) $(0, 1200)$, $(-40, 0)$, $(10, 1000)$ and $(0, 0)$. Only $(10, 1000)$ is sensible since $R, F > 0$.

26 (ii) $y = 90.91$, $x = 181.82$

(iii) A: x increases to 181.82, y initially decreases to a minimum and then increases to 90.91

B: Both x and y decrease to their equilibrium values.

C: x decreases to 181.92, y initially increases to a maximum and then decreases to 90.91

D: x decreases and y increases to their equilibrium values.

27 (i) All are $2.4 \times 10^{-10} \, \text{kg} \, l^{-1}$

(ii) 16.2 years

(iii) 16.2 years

28 (i) (a) $(1.5, -2.5)$

(b) $(-1, 1)$

(c) $(-1, -1)(-2, -2)$

Index